HALVOR

By

Peer O. Strømme

Translated from the Norwegian by
Inga Bredesen Norstog
edited by
Neil T. Eckstein

Including a Biographical Essay
Wisconsin's Native Son
By
Prof. Gerald Thorson

ISBN: 0-615-12409-7

Published by:
Grandview Books
5555 Grandview Road
Larsen, Wisconsin 54947

Printed in the United States by Morris Publishing
3212 East Highway 30
Kearney, NE 68847
1-800-650-7888

Editor's Preface

Peer Strømme's best-known novel, *Halvor,* appeared first in the Norwegian language newspaper, the Superior (Wisconsin) *Posten,* as a fictional serial from November of 1892 to June of 1893. Strømme was editor of the newspaper at that time, and the serialized novel helped to boost the circulation of this nearly defunct newspaper. In 1893 the novel first appeared in book form, published by B. Amundson of the Decorah *Posten* in an edition of 3000 copies. Several later editions of the novel as written originally in the Norwegian language helped to make the story well-known to many in the Norwegian-American community.

The first English translation of the novel by Inga Bredesen Norstog appeared in 1936 under the title *How Halvor Became a Minister,* a literal translation of Strømme's title, *Hvorledes Halvor Blev Prest.* I have chosen in this edition to shorten the title simply to *Halvor.* The term "minister" in our time has a somewhat different connotation than the term "prest" had in the Norwegian-American community of a century or more ago.

Mrs. Norstog's husband, Jon Norstog, was a well-known Norwegian-American poet, and Mrs. Norstog served as director of the Norwegian-American Historical Museum in Decorah, Iowa, from 1947 to 1959.

In 1960, a second English language version of the novel appeared under the auspices of the Luther College Press. This paperback version was edited and revised substantially by David T.

[i]

Nelson. Prof. Nelson had a long career as Professor of English at Luther College, and his edition appeared in time to help Luther College celebrate its centennial in 1961. In Prof. Nelson's own words, he "tightened up the story by omitting two chapters—'The American Saloon' and 'Trouble in the Congregation'—neither of which mentions the hero." He also cut out what he termed "minor irrelevant details to speed the story" and made other changes, including the names of several characters in the story. In the light of the college's forthcoming centennial and the anticipation of the story's usefulness in making students and other members of the Luther College community aware of their unique heritage, Prof. Nelson's revisions undoubtedly served a good purpose. Strømme wrote his novel in haste, and Nelson's revisions helped to make the story more readable to 20th century American readers.

In preparing this edition, however, I chose to revert to Mrs. Norstog's more literal translation of Strømme's original novel. In so doing, I did not hesitate to make minor changes from time to time which I felt could make the story a bit more readable or improve the flow of the language. I consulted both Strømme's original Norwegian version as well as David T. Nelson's 1960 translation from time to time in order to verify the changes in question, but the story as presented in this edition is basically Mrs. Norstog's translation, with only minor tinkering as I deemed necessary.

The underlying theme of the story, the coming of age, or the passage from childhood to adolescence to adulthood is a theme of universal appeal. Strømme was sometimes called the "Mark Twain" of Norwegian-American fictional writing. There is, to be sure, a kind of "Tom Sawyer-ish" quality to the novel, and Strømme's often sly and even impish sense of humor can still delight the modern reader.

There is also the appeal of the schoolboy narrative as told and retold in many works of fiction. As such, the novel will always have a very special relationship to Decorah and the Luther College community. The earlier two English versions came directly from this connection. This time, however, the edition is published in the birthplace community of Peer Strømme with a deliberate intention of helping residents of that community recover an important segment of their own heritage. I currently reside just a bit over a half a mile from Peer Strømme's place of birth in Winchester Township, Winnebago County, Wisconsin, the fictional "Springville" in eastern Wisconsin.

It has been pointed out that the minor character, Nils Klemmetsrud, in this novel is unique as a character type. Dripping with an unctuous piety, this pesky busy-body renders damning judgments upon his neighbors for the slightest provocations; yet his life often fails to live up to his vociferous professions. In a slightly tipsy state upon returning from town, he does not hesitate to upbraid Halvor's father over the lost condition of his soul. Within the confines of the ethnic settlement he is a constant source of turmoil and dissent, always cloaked in a veneer of super-piety. Predictably anti-clerical, he was the moving spirit in fomenting an undercurrent of dissent which eventually caused a tragic split in the congregation with two church structures standing side by side on the highest hill in the settlement.

I have chosen only a very few end-notes to explain terms which may baffle the modern reader who may be only marginally and vaguely familiar with the unique context of the extensive Norwegian-American community of more than a century ago. Peer Strømme was thoroughly at home in this community. He had a reputation as a "name-dropper," especially in his *Erindringer,* (Memoirs). In *Halvor* there are also references to a number of historical persons who figured prominently in the larger Norwegian-American community. I decided not to burden the modern reader with endless details of identification. Readers familiar with the larger cultural context will be able to identify some of these references, but such identification is not necessary for the more casual reader.

I want to acknowledge the valuable assistance which I received from a number of persons in preparing this edition for publication. My daughter, Jane Murphy, has given expert assistance in formatting the manuscript, in providing the cover photo which was taken at Norskedalen near Coon Valley, Wisconsin, and getting the book print-ready for the publishers. The back cover photo of Luther College as it appeared when 'Halvor' enrolled as a student in 1869 was provided by Rachel Vagts, the archivist at Luther College. The silhouette drawing of Peer Strømme which also appears on the back cover is from a ragged old dust cover of the 1936 edition which I inherited. Prof. Harland Nelson and Prof. David Nelson (son of the translator of the 1960 edition), both from Luther College, were helpful in giving some good advice about publishing this edition. I also wish to acknowledge the good work of Morris Publishers in producing the final product.

I realized that for many persons today the name of Peer Strømme is all but forgotten, and so I decided that it would be appropriate to include a helpful biographical essay written some years ago by the late Prof. Gerald Thorson of St. Olaf College. Prof. Thorson wrote his master's thesis at the University of Minnesota early in his career on Peer Strømme's life and works. I am grateful to Thea Yoder and her siblings for permission to include their father's essay in this edition of *Halvor*.

Finally, I wish to thank my wife, Marie, and other members of my family for their patience during the long hours which had to be devoted to preparing this book for publication.

Neil T. Eckstein, editor

Halvor

A Wealthy Immigrant

Søren Helgeson came to America in the late forties. It was said he possessed only what he wore on his back, and in one way this was true. But in reality he was rich. He had no money, to be sure; but he had what was more. He had wonderful health, great physical strength, a good conscience, a happy disposition, and an excellent appetite. He looked out upon the world through a pair of honest gray eyes which shone with the zest of living and with unconquerable courage. He feared God but no man, and he was his own master.

He had, moreover, a treasure at home in Tuddal, Telemark, which he would not exchange for all America. In a little tenant place in the shelter of Gausta Mountain, there was a certain wholesome and comely girl who had promised him in parting that she would come to him as soon as ever it could be managed. Only first he must make a home in the New World and send her a ticket. That, he thought, should not take long in America where gold was to be found in heaps and where good workers were at a premium. It had been hard, indeed, for Søren to leave Signe. But as it had been all he could do to scrape together enough money to get to the Promised Land himself there had been no other way. Signe had wept secretly at the thought of parting; but when the day came, and Søren in company with a few neighbors was about to leave for Skien to board a sailing vessel bound for America, she was very brave. She gave him a hand carved lunch box and a silk kerchief and said only, "How I wish we had the money so that I could go with you now. But we'll have to wait. So good-bye, Søren."

In those days it was no joke to cross the ocean. They were heroes, those Norwegian pioneers, who at that time had sufficient courage and faith to leave their poverty-ridden homes among the mountains and seek a living for themselves and their dear ones in what was to them an entirely new world, and to found there the New Norway which is our heritage and which we love and consider to be the best among a hundred lands.

That Søren and his friends had a most unpleasant time in crossing is indisputable. In fair weather it was not so bad, for then the women could at least have the pleasure of sitting on deck with their sick children sunning themselves and weeping. And when the weather was particularly fine they might even cheer up enough to talk among themselves about the homes they had left and to speculate as to what America was like. But in foul weather when they were compelled to stay below enduring stench and vermin and had to force themselves and the children to eat the dry food which they had brought along, it was—well, he who has tried it will not care to go through it again.

Søren was the life of the party during the long voyage. It was not so bad for him as he had only himself to take care of. He was, to be sure, so seasick the first day that he felt as though he was about to throw up his toenails. But even this was not an unmitigated evil, for it saved his food supply. Later he felt so well again that he could easily have eaten a mountain of food.

Søren had faith in himself and in his future in America, and he helped the rest to keep up their courage.

Between times he was occupied mostly with dreaming that he already owned a beautiful farm, possessing flocks of sheep and herds of cattle, with many shining dollars stored away in his chest; and that he had Signe in his arms.

The progress was so slow that they were getting desperate. They looked at the same endless ocean day after day and week after week. It was enough to drive one mad to have the wind always blowing from the wrong direction. Søren grew almost sick with longing for this loafer's existence to end. He ached to have a chance to show the Americans what a good worker he was. He looked at his big hands, straightened his strong back, and felt able to clear such a farm as could not be found in all of Telemark. It would surely not take long to save up enough to send for Signe. Then the main object would be won. And how he would work and save so that she might have comforts! Would they never get there and get started? Even the old sailor's trick of scratching the main mast and whistling for favorable winds failed. At any rate, it was two weeks before there were any results. And the wind might, of course, have turned anyway, even if Søren had not tried this device.

At last after thirteen long weeks the good ship landed at Quebec.

There was, of course, not one of the company who knew the language of the country, and they had but the faintest notion of where they were going. They knew only that they were going to a place called Wisconsin, where some people from their own part of Norway had already settled, and where great things were awaiting them. Many of the immigrants had about the same idea of America as was later expressed in doggerel verse about Ole Bull's colony in Pennsylvania.

Oh, Ole-Oleanna, that's the place for me.
No longer will I live in Norway's slavery.

There young pigs nicely roasted run about and say:
"How about roast pork for your dinner, Sir, today?"

There hens they say lay eggs much bigger than a haycock.
The rooster crows the time of day just like an eight-day clock.

The moon is always full at night like the bottom of a cask.
Right now I'm looking at him. My spyglass is my flask.

[3]

As was said, they were bound for Wisconsin; but where this was, or whether it was a parish or a district as large as all of Telemark, they knew not.

They were herded along like a flock of sheep. Confused and bewildered by all the new and strange things they had seen, and worn by the long and exhausting journey, they stood at last on the wharf at Milwaukee.

Here many of them were met by relatives or friends who had been in the country a year or two. But these did not look as if they had acquired their share of the great riches reputed to be heaped up all around. On the contrary, they were more ragged than they had ever been in poor old Norway, and they were shaking with a fever which had all but undone them.

Most of the immigrants were going to the homes of relatives or friends in Muskego where there had been a flourishing settlement for some years.

Anne Landsverk, one of Søren's fellow travelers, had a husband in America to whom she was going. He had left for America shortly after the wedding to make a home for her, and he had left her in blessed circumstance. Now she had come to him with their infant son. During the voyage she had been alternately elated and depressed; and she had been wondering continually how Ole was getting along, and if he would meet her in Milwaukee, and if he would think their son was beautiful, and so on.

When she reached Milwaukee at last, she looked around and her eyes filled with tears. No Ole was to be seen. Søren, who had been of great help to her on the voyage, stood beside her trying his best to comfort her. And there came Ole! He took his wife's hand in his; their eyes met and they trembled with happiness. And then, of course, she must show him the baby at once. With what bliss did she not lift the kerchief from its face, as holding the little fellow up for the father to see him, she asked if he would have known his child if he had found him along the road somewhere. Man and wife were so intensely happy that the world seemed to be a very good place after all. Søren was greeted most heartily by Ole who had known him in Norway. Anne never tired of telling Ole how good Søren had been to her, and how he had helped her with the baby and how he had kept up her courage during the terrible storm when she had been so frightened, for Søren, she said, wasn't afraid of a thing.

Ole had brought a wagon to fetch his family home. While he was busy with the luggage and waiting for the oxen to eat some hay, Søren took a little walk up town to see what he could see. Milwaukee was at that time no big city; but it was larger than Skien, the most sizeable town Søren had seen in Norway. What impressed him most was the fact that the people he saw did not look much different from those in Norway. They were about the same size, and they looked as if they might well have spoken Norwegian. The houses, too, were not unlike those he was accustomed to see. It seemed impossible to realize that he really was in a New World, and that the wide ocean rolled between Signe and him. How he wished he had brought her with him. His next thought was how good it would be to eat his fill. This was something he had not done for three months. His big, powerful body needed different food from that which he had brought along with him.

He found his way back to Anne and Ole who were now ready to start for Muskego. He was to go home with them for the present, and then he was to look for work. Anne took her place in the wagon, and off they started. It did not go very fast. Ole walked in front of the oxen with a long lash, shouting "Haw" and "Gee" and "Go long." Anne and Søren marveled at how proficient he had already become in English.

The very next day Søren began helping Ole with clearing the woods, while Anne worked about the house as if she had been there all her life.

Later in the summer Søren found work on the farm of an American of native stock who was farming on a big scale near

Honey Creek. He soon proved to be an unusually efficient worker, for he was used to toil, as he had lost both parents early in life and had worked out ever since. He was now not much over twenty, was strong and willing, and soon became so adept at swinging the flail that many years later Mr. Newman used to remark that if they only had such workmen as that Norwegian boy who worked for him some years before the war, harvesting machines would be superfluous. The lady of the house thought him a very big eater; but Mr. Newman contended that if he ate for two he worked for two, as well.

Søren stayed with these people for two years. The first winter, since he was not kept so busy as he had been during the summer, he made a business of trying to learn English. As he never did things by halves, he went at this task, too, with all his might. The teacher of the nearby school boarded at Newman's. She enjoyed talking to the big, blond immigrant, and was therefore willing to help him evenings. For a short time there were also evening classes in the schoolhouse which Søren and other grown-ups frequented. Many poked fun at him for his queer clothes and peculiar speech. As a rule he paid no attention, but if their remarks became too personal he occasionally responded with some pointed remarks of his own. Or, if the merriment at his expense went too far, he would tackle his tormenters in true Telemark style and send them sprawling to the ground.

His pay the first year was only five dollars a month, so it was little he could save. But the second year he got a little raise. And at last the time came to ask Mr. Newman for the wages due him. He used what was necessary to buy the ticket which he sent at once to that little tenant place in Tuddal to Signe who was waiting so eagerly for it. When this was accomplished Søren felt proud and happy.

His next task was to build a home in preparation for Signe's coming. In Muskego and the surrounding territory, all public lands were taken; but farther north in the so-called *Indiland*[1] there were still some to be had. Within the thick forest there was already a start of a Norwegian settlement called Springville. Some of Søren's acquaintances from the trip had settled there; and presently he joined them. The trip was cheap, as he made it on foot, carrying his goods in a sack. He was dead tired when at the end of the fourth day he arrived at the home of Ole Kjeldalen, the leading citizen of Springville. Besides Kjeldalen there were a number of sturdy Norwegians living in the woods. There were Skogen, and Lia, and Børthe, and Sigvat Halvorson. The last named was a relative of Kjeldalen's who later became the first Norwegian farmer elected to Congress. And, then, there were Hallingen, the Toten Brothers, Thrond Valdris, and Hatlevik-Ole, and the not to be forgotten Klemmetsrud, a man known for his great piety. One of his sons later became one of the leading clergymen of Hauge's Synod; and his daughter married the even better known lay-preacher named Ole Maaseryg.

In this settlement our friend Søren Helgeson took 160 acres of land which was covered with a fine stand of oak trees. He built a little cabin at once, and began to clear the woods around it. The thought that he was building a home for Signe gave him double strength and he worked like a slave from dawn to dusk. Late at night, when the day's work was done, he would walk through the woods to old Kjeldalen's for supper. This consisted of corn meal mush and milk. Then he would go to bed up in the loft and fight mosquitoes until he was tired enough to sleep in spite of their bites.

One day word came that Signe, God bless her, had already arrived at Muskego; and, what was better still, that she was coming to Springville at once in company with a family from Muskego.

Søren worked, and longed, and dreamed. And one evening when he got to Kjeldalen's he saw that something had happened. The wife who sat milking said, "Who do you think is here?" Then she would say no more. Søren stepped into the tiny house, but there was no one there. Yes, there was someone behind the door; and when he looked, there stood Signe lovely and happy, with tears in her eyes. Norwegians of their class are not given to caressing each other. It is not unusual for man and wife to live together happily for years without ever kissing each other. A husband returning from an absence of many weeks is likely to say only, "Hello, how are you?" and that is all there is to it. We know a boy who when he was only twelve years old had to leave home to be gone two years. And yet his mother only clasped his hand and said, "Goodbye, my boy." But when he was gone, she grieved until she became ill. Søren and Signe said only "Hello," and made a few commonplace remarks to one another; but they were happy, indeed. Signe looked with pride at the tall, strong man who had acquired blond whiskers since she had last seen him. He in turn devoured her with shining eyes from top to toe. He could not look at her long enough. And she *was* beautiful; there was no denying it. She was perhaps a little too buxom, but she had regular features—heavy, dark hair, and a pair of eyes in which shone faith and love enough to spoil ten men. Søren's impulse was to clasp her to his heart, but he dared not; he must wait.

Now the family came in and all listened with speechless interest to all that Signe had to tell about friends and relatives in the old country.

The Bethel Congregation

The next day Signe accompanied Søren to their future home and helped him put it in order. They would have liked to be married at once. But unfortunately there was no minister within reach. Ole Kjeldalen agreed with Søren that there was no other way than to go to an American justice of the peace to be married civilly or *squared*.[2] But Signe disapproved of this plan. She was not sure that she would be really married in that case. And Thrond Knudson Valdrisen, who was a much traveled man, insisted that such *squaring* was pure heathendom which would never be permitted by the pastor at home in Slidre – Harbitz was his name.

This was indeed a quandary. But help soon appeared. It was not long before word was sent from house to house that on the coming Sunday a genuine Norwegian minister was coming to Springville. He was to conduct services at Ole Kjeldalen's house and attempt to organize a congregation.

It was a great day for the pioneers when they were able to come together for the first time in their new home and hear a sermon by a Norwegian Lutheran pastor. Some of them had not only one, but several children who had not "got a name." Now they brought them all along. Never before had hymn singing sounded so beautiful. They sang in every key and all out of time. Gunhild Knudson was three words behind the rest at the close of the first stanza so that she sang "Thee and Hea-ea-eaven" all alone. But no one minded in the least. The only one who took offense was

Klemmetsrud. He had long known that Gunhild was not a converted child of God, and that her singing, therefore, was naught but sounding brass and tinkling cymbal. The rest were happy and felt as if they were at home in dear old Norway. And when Pastor Preus stepped forward and began his sermon they listened with both ears and mouths. They could, of course, tell at once that he was a real minister; for he had the very same garb as the clergymen of Norway wore. His *stas*, namely the black gown and white ruff, were proof that he was a *stas* clergyman and belonged to the *stas* church.[3]

Gently, and in simple words, he told them that they could not live on bread alone here any more than in the Old World; and he urged them first and foremost to preserve the faith of their fathers.

The infants who were to be baptized howled most distressingly. It was dreadfully hot in the room and the mothers had dressed the poor things in their bravest array, so it was not to be wondered at that they cried. Since the pastor could not hold both ears and nose and at the same time perform the rites of baptism he had no choice but to make the best of things.

Short as was the time these parents had been in America, they had, nevertheless, already learned that it would not do to give their children honest Norwegian names. They were afraid the Yankees might not be able to pronounce them. Ingeborg, therefore, became Isabelle; Kari, Katie; and such a good name as Sigrid was changed to Sarah or Sallie. A boy, moreover, who was to be named for his grandfather Harald, went his way rejoicing in the name Horace.

But when the service was over and food had been partaken of, the men gathered together to consider the founding of a congregation. Pastor Preus explained to them what the procedure must be under free church conditions.

Everyone appeared to be much in favor of organizing. Of course they needed a pastor so that their children might be christened and confirmed; otherwise they would simply revert to heathendom. Thrond Knudson, however, had his doubts as to whether baptizing and such things were necessary in America where there was so much land which did not belong to any parish at all, and where there really were people who possessed names without having been baptized, wherever in the world they might have got them from. But he did not dare express such thoughts out loud. He merely intimated that he should like very much to find out what Pastor Harbitz would have thought of this whole business. And then there was Nils Klemmetsrud who had been influenced by the religious revival of Western Norway. He was a very pious man in both speech and life, especially in the former; and during the sermon strong doubts had arisen in his mind as to whether Pastor Preus really was converted. Why, the man had not even shed a tear; and, besides, he had read a part of his sermon from a manuscript. It certainly looked as if he had depended upon his book learning alone.

Klemmetsrud was, moreover, suspicious of all these pesky *stas* clergymen and would have preferred that they had asked Elling Eielson to come. But as he knew that no one would agree with him he thought it best to fall in with the rest. All the men present now signed a document in which they declared that they were organizing a congregation to be known as Bethel Norwegian Lutheran Congregation in Springville, Wisconsin.

At one juncture it had looked as if the whole project would fall through. It had first been proposed to name the congregation Hitterdal Congregation since most of the members had come from Hitterdal in Norway. At this an uproar arose. Thrond Knudson was from Valders. He was a small, lame man with a stubborn disposition and a head full of whims and superstitions. He had somehow strayed over into Springville from the new Valdris settlement at Manitowoc, for which reason he was usually called Valdrisen.

He now declared that neither he nor Gunhild, his wife, would belong to a congregation named Hitterdal. He was backed in this objection by Klemmetsrud, who felt that this question was a matter of conscience. He did not consider Hitterdal a Christian name. He moved that the congregation be called Bethel, that being a name dear to all children of God. Thrond seconded the motion. He did not know exactly what Bethel meant, not having heard the word before. But he felt sure that there was nothing derogatory to the people from Valders, and they were certainly every bit as good as Telemarkings. He wished they could have heard Pastor Harbitz preach. There was not his superior in all Norway. He could have had his choice of any parish in the land but Valders was good enough for him.

For the sake of peace all agreed to call the congregation Bethel, but Preus was actually ungodly enough to tell Klemmetsrud to his face that there was nothing wicked about calling a congregation Hitterdal.

That reef having been cleared, the congregation was established with Kjeldalen, the Toten brothers, and Klemmetsrud as trustees. In electing these men, due attention had been given to geographical origin; for they represented Telemark, Toten, and Stavanger.

It was a bitter disappointment to Thrond Knudson that he was not elected. But he swallowed his vexation and consoled himself with the thought that the others certainly did not have better prospects of getting to Heaven than he, especially not that Totning who was known to be given to drinking and profanity and who was, besides, so addicted to card playing that it had become proverbial. It was told that one night his oxen had come home from town alone while he lay sleeping by the roadside. And when a couple of neighbors found him and tried to wake him up he answered only, "If I'd known you were going to play that card I'd a laid on the queen." If such a man could be elected trustee, Thrond certainly thought he was good enough for the position. As the new congregation did not feel able to support a minister to start with, it was promised that Pastor Duus would visit it three or four times a year.

After the services and business meeting, when nearly everyone had left, Søren Helgeson went over to Pastor Preus and asked to speak to him.

"Certainly," said the minister. "What did you wish?"

"Oh, I just wanted to ask if Pastor Preus would perform a service for me. I wish to change my condition." The minister thought at first that he had before him a penitent sinner who wished to change his way of life. He soon realized, however, that it was something entirely different. The matter was soon settled; the Kjeldalens assuring him that everything was as it should be. Then Søren and Signe stepped forward and were married.

Ole Kjeldalen had gone to the trouble of making a low stool for the occasion. Covered with a sheet, it served as a hassock. So nothing was amiss, except Signe answered, "No," when she was asked if she could conscientiously say she had never given her troth to any man now living. But when the question was explained she answered, "Yes."

In the evening the bridal pair went to their home, and Søren was as proud as a king.

Family Joys

The house to which Søren Helgeson brought his young bride was humble enough to look at. It lay in the thick forest with only a small cleared space around it. And even on this small spot the great black stumps were still standing, awaiting the time when they would have rotted sufficiently to be pulled out with oxen and a log chain. The house, like all others in the settlement, was timbered of great oak logs. It had only one room with a loft above it. The furniture consisted of some home-made benches, a table, a cook stove, and a bed. The last named stood in one corner under the ladder leading to the loft. In the floor was a trap door leading to a little hole in the ground which served as a cellar. Near the door a shelf was nailed to the wall. On it was a wash bowl with a piece of yellow soap beside it. Up close to the beams there was also a shelf on which lay nails, auger, broad axe, and other tools. And, over by the stove there was still another shelf for kitchen utensils. Clothes were hung on the wall or folded away in a chest at the foot of the bed. On the table lay a Bible which Signe had brought from Norway and another book entitled *The Saints' Eternal Rest*, both of which had to be moved to the bed when the table was to be set.

This was the whole array; but the two who possessed it had also faith and love; and they needed nothing more. They were, moreover, capable and industrious and soon began to get ahead. Søren was, besides, an intelligent fellow who took pride in learning the ways of the land so that he soon became a leader. When the town was organized, he was elected justice of the peace in spite of his youth. It was not long before he became legal advisor for the neighbors, writing their notes, drawing up deeds and other papers. He was honest in all his dealings and was respected by all.

The winter after the wedding, Signe, poor girl, was not always so well. It seemed as if she could not relish her food, especially mornings. This was not strange, considering that it consisted of nothing but pork and potatoes except for supper, when there was corn meal mush. Often when Søren came home he found her with tears in her eyes. As spring advanced she felt better, but by mid-summer she was no longer able to help with the outdoor work. One evening, as she stood with her arms folded beneath her breast looking at her husband as he hoed the potatoes, she suddenly felt ill and said, "Søren, it is best that you fetch Gunhild Knudson." Søren helped her into the house and ran as fast as he could over to Valdrisen's house. Since he came over in such haste, the knowing Gunhild was quick to sense what was up. She was ready at once and went with him with a bottle of camphor and whiskey in her hand.

Gunhild was the only real midwife of the settlement. There was, to be sure, Kari Sandbakken, who had occasionally had the presumption to officiate in that capacity; but Gunhild could not for the life of her see how anyone who knew how easily things might go wrong could entrust herself to such clumsy handling.

Gunhild's calling brought her much joy, and she was proud of her ability. She was never so completely happy as when sitting with a saucer full of coffee balanced on her finger tips relating all the circumstances of the last case at which she had officiated.. She had a mother's heart for all the many children whom she had helped bring into the world. When they grew up she gave them good advice, always basing her right to do so by saying, "You know, I was the first one who saw you; it was me who received you when you came into the world."

[15]

In the present case all went well, but Søren was so overcome by fear that he tried to run away every once in a while. Gunhild really had to scold him roundly for being such poor help to her—great, big, good-for-nothing that he was!

The next day, when Gunhild had procured a girl to take care of Signe, Soren went back to his work again in the potato patch. He was somewhat more serious than before. He would often stop and look into the air vacantly, and even more often, walk to the door to see if Signe and the boy were asleep.

The rumor of this event traveled fast, for Gunhild at once made errands to a number of the neighbors and told them the news that Signe had got a son. He was, she said, a big, strong boy; although she thought he had come a few days too early. This was due she thought to the fact that Signe had been frightened when Klemmetsrud had come into the house one evening when she was alone. He was on his way home from town and was slightly tipsy, and he had begun to weep over the lost condition of Søren's soul. Signe had exerted herself beyond her strength to get him to go home.

The neighbor women were so kind that at first it was hard for Signe to regain her strength. Each one of them brought a great bowl of cream mush or rømmegraut, and some brought home-brewed ale. Then they would sit urging her to eat while they entertained her by telling the details of their own experiences in similar circumstances.

All this kindness nearly killed the poor woman. For, of course, she must at least taste the mush which each one brought. And it was heavy food. It tastes so very good but one gets full long before one has had enough. And the richer the mush was, the more it was relished. It must at least "butter itself" in the kettle. And then butter was even added and the whole sprinkled with brown sugar and cinnamon.

But Signe had a strong constitution and recovered in spite of all the kindness shown her. Soon she was up and around again attending to her household duties. When she and Søren were alone evenings all pain was forgotten as in tranquil joy they gazed at the boy nursing so avidly at her breast. Never had Søren seen so lovely a sight. He would gently pinch the baby's face, stroke the mother's hair and he felt himself to be the richest man in all the world. He made up his mind that he would work like a beaver. Signe must have everything to make her happy. He would never say an unkind word to her. And when the boy grew up he should be sent to school and be educated to become a minister or a lawyer, or something equally great, so that no one would dream that he was the son of a Norwegian immigrant who had come to America without a dollar in his pocket.

As luck would have it news soon came that Pastor Duus was coming to conduct services, so Søren and Signe had a chance to have their boy christened. He was named Halvor. Gunhild Knudson who had brought him into the world was his godmother—an honor she always set great store by. She was the godmother of nearly all the children in the community.

As was customary, Søren and Signe had a christening party. After the services, a number of the neighbors went home with them and were treated to cream mush. As the evening advanced more and more people came uninvited. Anyone might come to a christening, with the understanding, of course, that he bring a gift for the child—an article of apparel, or a sum of money, according to his means.

The men sat outside along the wall, and as usual it was Thrond Knudson who led the conversation. He was dreadfully ignorant and had the credulity which goes with ignorance. His respect for book learning was prodigious. For Søren, in particular, his awe was great because of the fact that Søren had already learned to read and write English. Thrond often remarked that if he had as much learning as

[17]

Søren he would certainly not be toiling like a plain farmer. He would go to the city and earn money like grass. He had, moreover, considerable native sagacity, having dabbled in a little of everything. Remedies he knew for all sorts of ailments, particularly those of cattle. His pet medicine was oil of spike in which he had a faith that was nothing short of pathetic. During his sojourn in Manitowoc County he had had a great deal to do with Indians and he could tell many strange things about them. He did not like their ways, but he always excused them by saying, "But then, you know, they are descended from heathen."

He firmly believed that ministers possessed the "black book" and could do whatever they chose and that there was nothing under the sun that they did not know.

On this Sunday evening Thrond was in his element. Among the yarns which he told was this one:

"It was just the year before I went to America. Another boy and me was digging a well; and way down deep in the earth we found a little box; and in this box was a little bottle; and in this bottle was a little animal as big as my little finger. We took the bottle to the minister—Pastor Harbitz it was—and asked him what the dickens it was. Harbitz sent it in to Kristiania, and it was not long before it came back with the strictest orders from the government and the professors for God's sake not to open it but to bury it just where we found it."

"Well, what was it that was in the bottle?" asked Pastor Duus.

"You sure must know that, being you are a minister."

"No, I really don't. So you may as well tell us."

"I can't believe you don't know. It was, of course, a little devil that was in the bottle. And Pastor Harbitz made us bury it, and quick, too. And this was just the year before I went to America."

Later on, when the preacher had left, the fun began. Hans Skogen had brought his fiddle. He sat down to tune it while the floor was being cleared in order that the young folks might dance.

Klemmetsrud told them sternly that it would be better if they thought of their immortal souls. But no one paid the slightest attention to him. When the floor was cleared, the men walked over to the bed one by one and laid their gifts upon it. Several of them who wanted to show what great fellows they were gave up to five dollars. One dollar was the rule, however. Then the dancing began. Signe had to dance the first dance to show that she was as spry as ever, as was the custom.

In the meantime the men sat outside drinking and singing ballads. Thrond knew a good one called the Valdris Song, in which the hero, who had just come to America, celebrates his prowess as a worker and the amazement of the Yankees over his ability. The stanza that was most appreciated was the one in which he boasts of his proficiency in English:

For when the Yankees asked what was my name,
I always hit the nail upon the head by answering,
"Oh, yes, Sir."

It was sung to the tune of *Dei vil altid klaga og kyta* and the audience joined in the chorus.

Next old Hatleviken in his drawling Sogning dialect sang a song, the first stanza beginning as follows:

Come hither, my friends who would hea-ear my ta-ale.
A song I shall sing that is lacking in mirth.
I call ye all friend whom my song may rega-ale
Although I am only a peasant by birth.

Experience hath proved what old Solomon sai-aid,
Believe not a woman. Her word hath no worth
He, too, was seduced, and by women misle-ed.
Although he was only a peasant by birth.

And then there was more balladry which they could all sing, as it had been composed by a local rhymester and described people of the community. It was considered a masterpiece and began thus:

South of Baklestulen an island you will see,
Its name it is Cuba; it belongs to Ole Lee;
And farther to the south lives a man and his wife,
He's the son of Halvor Kjeldalen as sure as your life.

While the dancing was growing noisier inside of the house, trouble was brewing outside among the men. Many of them had brought alcohol with them from home which they mixed with the home-brewed ale. Becoming tipsy they grew quarrelsome and started calling each other names.

Among those present was Ole Findreng. It had been rumored that he had once stolen a whetstone and a clevis from a neighbor's field. For this reason he had been nicknamed "Whetstone-Ole." Aanun Strand could not resist taunting him with sundry covert remarks about a whetstone. In the sweetest and most innocent tone he asked, "Say, Ole, what do you think? Can a whetstone float in water?"

In an instant they were in the thick of a fight. Women screamed and begged someone to stop them before someone was hurt. Søren took hold of both belligerents by the collar and ordered them to behave themselves. As this did no good, he sent them both sprawling to the ground in different directions. "Whetstone-Ole" had fared the worse of the two and was bleeding profusely. But after he had washed and had had another drink he swaggered around and swore that he would have made short work of Aanun if it had only not been too dark to see what one was doing.

At last, when all had left, and Søren and Signe were in bed, Signe said, "I don't think such parties are any fun."

"Right you are," replied Søren. "But you know how it is with the first child. It's going to be the last time, though. I'll never have such rowdiness in this house again."

Then Signe said a little hesitantly, "Oh, Søren, you're not getting too fond of strong drink, are you?"

"No," said Søren. "I admit I've had a little too much to drink tonight. But this is the last time. I give you my word."

And that promise was kept.

Sorrow

Søren Helgeson had been most fortunate in getting a good piece of land, but it was a hard task to clear it. As he was unbelievably industrious, the cleared space around his house grew steadily larger, and it looked as if his dream of wealth was to be realized. Among the many oak stumps he planted potatoes and corn, sowed oats and some wheat. He prospered, and he and his wife were happy and thankful that they had taken up their abode in America. The homesickness which caused them so much pain the first year or two had gradually worn off. But now Søren received a blow from which he never recovered.

When little Halvor was two years old and Signe again was with child, it happened one night that she was gored by one of the oxen, so that Søren had to carry her in and lay her on the bed. He rushed off to fetch Gunhild Knudson and when he returned he found Signe in great pain. Soon after Gunhild arrived the child was born. But Gunhild's practiced eye soon saw that it could not live. At once she got a bowl of water and baptized it, for nothing in the world would she have burdened her conscience by allowing a child to go out of the world unchristened. Such a thing had happened once in her presence and she had suffered much on account of it, for Klemmetsrud had given her to understand that it was very questionable if forgiveness could be obtained for that sin.

Gunhild had not been mistaken. During the night the child died. When Signe, in a weak voice, asked to see it and they had to tell her that it had been taken up to the Father's House above, she answered only that she would soon go there too. She lay perfectly quiet until morning. Then she began to repeat the Lord's Prayer aloud.

"You aren't going to leave me, are you?" asked Søren as he stood by her bed with his gaze fixed upon her. Then she asked for little Halvor. They lifted him from the cradle and held him up to her. Then she took hold of Søren's hand, and gave a deep sigh; after a short while, another; and then Gunhild said in a slow, solemn way that all was over. That was all. It has happened very often and it hurt Søren Helgeson quite as much as it does the President of the United States, only one does not say so much about it.

Søren bowed his head over the bed; then he straightened up and went out to the chopping block. He took the broad axe which lay there and went over to the barn wall where the vicious ox stood chewing his cud, and before the animal knew what had happened he received a blow between the eyes that felled him to the ground. Søren gave him a couple of more blows to be sure he would never rise again. Then laying the axe away, he went in, picked up little Halvor in his arms, sat down on the bench and drew a breath so convulsive that Gunhild was frightened. She could only comfort him by saying that it must be that Signe's time had come.

Søren sat for a while as if turned to stone, but then he braced himself up and asked Gunhild in a humble voice to do whatever needed to be done. Word was sent for Kari Sandbakken who was always present on such occasions. Thrond came and helped Søren make the coffin and his son Knud was sent around to invite the neighbors to the funeral.

They came in the forenoon, quietly and solemnly. Everyone was to have dinner before he went to the cemetery. As the table was small and the guests many, this took a long time. All were too modest to be seated at the first table, and they had to be persuaded to do so one by one, and with difficulty. When the most prominent men at last were seated, old Hatleviken, who was the parish clerk, and who always acted as master of ceremonies, took a position at one end of the table and sang *Who Knows How Soon My Life May End* as slowly as he was able. The old man had been song leader in the church at Lyster and he followed the custom of that place most scrupulously.

When he had finished the stanza, he said, "Now that ye good people are seated, let each say grace in his customary way—'The Eyes of All Wait Upon Thee, O Lord.'" When all had repeated this silently or had pretended to do so, he said, "Please help yourself, good people, to the food that has been prepared for you." Then he watched to see when all were satisfied, and said, "If ye are all satisfied, good people, ye must not forget to thank God for the food. Let each give thanks in his customary way: 'Thank the Lord, for He is good.'" And when this was done he continued: "May the food benefit you, good people all. Let each thank his friend and neighbor for the food by word as well as by handshake." Then he got up and, shaking hands with the neighbor to the right and to the left, thanked them for the food. Now the table was cleared in all haste and set for the next group. At this setting and those which followed he was not quite so particular about following the rules in every detail, but even so it was almost evening before the dinner was over.

The coffin in which Signe lay was set forth on the bench in the middle of the room, and then they made ready to start out. Ole Kjeldalen, who was only one of the settlers who had got so far as to have horses, drew up before the door. The coffin was carried out, the clerk heading the procession and singing a hymn. By virtue of his office he seated himself on the wagon seat with Ole Kjeldalen, and the procession started off—the wagon ahead and the rest following afoot, for the distance was short. Søren walked directly behind the wagon.

On a hillside at one corner of Kjeldalen's farm, land for a cemetery had been marked off with the intention that a church should be built there in time. A few graves were already there, marked by black-painted, wooden crosses. The coffin was lifted off from the wagon and lowered while they sang *No Better Journey I Take Than That Which Leads Me Home to God.* Søren felt as if his heart went down with the coffin and remained in the grave when it was filled in.

Ole Kjeldalen went over to where Søren stood and invited him to go home with him. But Søren declined with thanks, saying that he preferred to go to his own home. He went alone toward his house and on the way he repeated again and again a line of the only English song he knew, *O, How I Loved Her None Can Tell.* On reaching home he sat down and began to talk to little Halvor who was too young to realize what they both had lost. How good and loving she always had been, God bless her! With a pain he recollected that he had once found fault with her for not being neat enough in her cooking. How hard it seemed that she should die just now when the burden of poverty was lifted and he was about to make a more attractive home for her. It was also a bitter thing that she had to be buried without the presence of a minister to express the Christian hope of resurrection. Søren was sensible enough to know that Signe rested quite as well without this; but, nevertheless, he would have been so glad if Pastor Duus had been near enough to have been sent for.

Mrs. Sandbakken, who had undertaken to take care of his house temporarily, arrived and began to get supper. And then Klemmetsrud came. He sat down and heaved a great sigh which was intended to convey sympathy. Then he started to exhort Søren not to take his loss too hard, but to be resigned to God's will and to be comforted by the thought that Signe's soul perhaps was saved.

Søren grew indignant and told Klemmetsrud that he needed no comfort on that score. He hadn't the slightest doubt but that Signe had gone straight home to God. And then he told Klemmetsrud that he preferred to be alone.

Klemmetsrud grew thoughtful and began to have his doubts as to the state of Søren's soul. But Søren sat long alone, brooding darkly. Then light came to him and he smiled an almost happy smile as he undressed Halvor and told him that Mother and Baby Sister were now in Heaven with God and were happy.

Halvor Grows Up

Søren became inordinately fond of his boy—his dearest remembrance of Signe. Wherever he went the boy had to go with him; and little by little, as Halvor grew, there developed a strangely intimate comradeship between them. It was not to be wondered at, as each was all the other had. Søren secured the help of a childless couple who had just come from Norway to help about the house and farm. He could, therefore, always leave the boy at home when he had an errand to the neighbors. But he could not stand to be separated from him even for a short time unless it was absolutely necessary. Even when he was only out in the field alone he hurried home to look after Halvor. Very early the boy learned all about the mother whom he had forgotten—how beautiful and kind she was; and he learned to think of her as a white-clad angel who, with a baby in her arms, was sitting up in Heaven and with her gentle eyes was watching him and his father wherever they might be. He learned that it would grieve her if he did anything wrong, and he would not want to cause her sorrow for anything in the world. With his love and admiration for his big, strong father there was mingled a sort of pity, for he discerned that for some reason his father was not a happy man. He was, to be sure, always kind and talked a great deal to his son. But otherwise he was silent and brooding.

In this way time passed until Halvor was six years of age and had already started to attend the district school. At this time a change came which the boy at first could not understand. The couple who had lived in Søren's house moved out as the man had secured a piece of land for himself, and now Søren engaged a daughter of Kari Sandbakken to keep house for him. Halvor did not like her because she always made him feel that he was in the way. But for some reason or other Søren and she often sat talking together, and one day while the boy was in school they went over to Kjeldalen's where Pastor Brandt just then happened to be stopping on his way to "Indiland." When Halvor came home from school he found his father and Anne sitting at the table dressed in their best and looking self-conscious. Søren called the boy over to him and told him that hereafter he must call Anne mother. But Halvor would not consent to that. He had never heard of anyone having more than one mother. And his mother was in Heaven; that he knew very well. In the evening, when he was put to bed up in the loft, he could not imagine what the reason could be. He felt utterly wretched and forsaken until his father came up and talked to him until he fell asleep.

It was not long, however, before he was awakened and frightened nearly out of his wits. Pandemonium had suddenly broken out all around the house. He had heard of the Indians and thought that they had come to kill him. Hoarse shouting and bellowing mingled with the clang of cowbells and tin pans. Occasionally a shot rang out.

Søren had been quietly married, and this was the punishment. This howling mob had come to "charivari." Søren went out and begged them to go home, only to be told that they would not think of such a thing until he had treated them to drinks all around. This Søren refused to do. For one thing he did not have any brandy in the house. Then the horrible din started up again. Some boys succeeded in getting a window open and let a pig into the house. Others amused themselves by uprooting some young apple trees that had just got a nice start.

Søren's wagon was taken apart and the different pieces hidden in every direction. Not until it was past midnight did they tire of the fun. At last when Søren had appeared in the doorway with his bride at his side to placate the crowd and had said that if they would leave he should thank them very much, but if they would not he would shoot. Finally the rowdies departed.

This foolish custom which in Norwegian-English is called "charivariing" was in those days a much enjoyed pastime, especially at weddings of which the public did not approve for one reason or another, or when some well-to-do person got married without giving a wedding party commensurate with his means or standing in life.

This idiocy has now very nearly gone out of fashion, the many accidents connected with the fun having brought about its passing. At a wedding in Manitowoc County it happened that the bride's father, one of the most respected citizens of the community, was killed by a stray bullet while he was out remonstrating with the roisterers. On a similar occasion at Washington Prairie the man of the house went and ordered the mob to go home. When they refused, he shot a bullet into the crowd and killed a young man on the spot.

Halvor was jealous of his new mother. What right had she to take his place? He soon grew used to calling her mother; but like her, he could not. The first time she punished him for some minor offense he grew so angry that he threw himself flat on the ground and kicked and screamed. When Søren arrived on the scene, he said mildly to the boy, "If you do not want to grieve Father you must mind Mother." Then he went into the house and said, "I want you to understand this, Anne, that you must be good to Halvor. If he needs a spanking, I'll give it to him myself."

From this time on Halvor was for one reason or another left more and more to himself. His father seemed to go to town very often, and when he came home he always talked about the war which had just broken out, intimating that he, too, was thinking about going to fight for the abolition of slavery.

In the summer time, Halvor's life was a pleasant one in spite of his loneliness. He could not stay indoors because then he was in his mother's way, but he found many pleasant diversions outdoors.

In the morning he must first drive the cows down the run to the marsh pasture where they were to feed. In this meadow there was a little pool in which he could wade and catch tadpoles. He caught one that had just begun to sprout legs. He carried it home and when his father told him that tadpoles turned into frogs he became more interested in the creatures than ever. Then, too, he knew about all the birds' nests around his home. He knew exactly how many eggs there were in each and watched their hatching with fatherly interest. Snakes he did not like, and he had many a battle with them. Among the first things he had learned from his godmother, Gunhild Knudson, was that snakes should be killed because it was a snake that had induced Eve to eat of the forbidden fruit in Paradise. While still very young he learned the trick of taking a snake by the tail and cracking it just as his father did the whip over the backs of his oxen, so that the poor snake's head flew off. Another favorite sport was the game of seesawing toads. A board was laid across a block; the toad was put on one end of the board; then the other end was struck so hard with a club that the toad was thrown high into the air.

Gunhild, who gave him his first instruction in the Christian faith, soon taught him that it was a sin to seesaw toads. Much other religious instruction he received from her as well, namely that it was a sin to whistle, to walk backwards, and to whittle on Sunday. To whistle was to call upon the Evil One; to walk backwards was to wish one's mother in hell. Occasionally Halvor ventured to do these things when no one saw or heard him, but he suffered terribly from pangs of conscience when he did so. The most dangerous of all these practices was to whittle on Sunday because Gunhild had told him that all the whittlings would be burned on his hand in the next world.

Since Halvor was a very conscientious little boy who did not like the prospect of having his hand burned, he was very careful not to whittle on Sunday. When it seemed absolutely necessary to cut a stick off on that day, he would first select a lonely spot and then saw it off, taking care to make as few whittlings as possible. These he would gather together very carefully and either scatter them to the winds or trample them into the ground, thinking that if God really could find them and burn them on his hand he would have to stand the pain. There was not enough to make a big fire anyway.

On weekdays, when he had driven the cows to the marsh meadow, the next thing was to get started for the schoolhouse, a little log building on the highway. At school Halvor did very well, and it was not long before he could tell his father a great many strange things that he had never heard of before. On an evening, the boy would often sit outdoors alone and think about George Washington who was the father of all America. Then his thoughts would turn to his own father who, he knew, was much stronger and wiser than Washington. Or, he would gaze through the openings in the woods to see the many pillars of smoke rising from as many farms, all of them kindled for the purpose of keeping the mosquitoes away while the cows were being milked. Sometimes he would chase the fireflies that flashed hither and thither among the trees. Every now and then he would put his ear to the ground to see if he could hear his father's wagon wheels on their way home from town. It could be heard at a great distance, for the road was very uneven, being built by laying logs side by side over the swampy stretches. And great was the joy when his father arrived. There was always a treat for him—either an apple or some candy. Just think: on his birthday Halvor got a pencil and a folding pocket knife, the edge of which his father had filed down a little for safety's sake. Halvor liked it none the less for that, and he hid it and the pencil carefully in a crack in the wall near his bed in the loft.

The first Christmas after his new mother came was an unusually happy one for Halvor. It was not because Anne had grown more fond of him. Quite the contrary. She was cross and irritable. But, as if to compensate for this, his father was always thinking of new ways to please him and to show him that the two of them at least were as good friends as ever. On Christmas Eve the boy was actually allowed to hang up his stocking to see if anything would find its way into it during the night. He woke up often during the night wondering what Santa might bring, and early in the morning he scrambled out of bed to look. Oh, boy! His stocking was full of cakes and candy, and beside it stood a tin horse and a pair of boots, the toes of which were tipped with copper to make them last longer. His father told him to go and thank his mother, too. Anne remarked that it was strange how rich Søren always was when there was something that the boy wanted. "Well," replied Søren, " I guess I can afford to spend a few pennies at Christmas time. It's my own money."

When spring came Søren again began to talk about going to war. A great number of the neighbors had gone and he felt it his duty to go, too. It was a disgrace for him to stay quietly at home. But Anne wept and expostulated. He could not possibly go and leave her in her present condition. There was nothing for it; Søren had to resign himself to staying at home. It seemed to Halvor at this time that his mother was more given to nagging than ever. She had a soft, high pitched, droning voice; and her fluency was amazing.

"I don't claim to know very much, but I do say that as I see things and according to my judgment—and I realize that I know very little—but anyway I think in my own simple way that it is wrong of you, Søren, to think about going to war now. You must at least wait until it is over, for I have a feeling that you will soon be a widower again. And then you can go wherever you please and take that boy of yours that you are so fond of although I can't see for the life of me that he is any better than any other boy except at cutting up—but not that I know anything, but I just want to tell you this, that if you go away now you are committing a great sin."

Søren listened patiently until she was through.

"Yes, yes, Anne, of course I'll stay at home. There's nothing more to be said about that. And you'll see that you'll come through it all right. Such things happen every day. And anyway, it isn't Halvor's fault.

And then it was the same old story. Halvor was given permission to spend the night at Thrond Knudson's; something he considered a great treat because it was always so pleasant there. When they had mush for supper Gunhild always let him scrape the kettle. They had, moreover, a half grown son named Knud who was old enough to use tobacco and to swear when his father was not around, for which reason Halvor looked up to him with great admiration.

When Halvor came down from the loft the next morning Gunhild told him that he might run home now. He had got a little sister, she said, and they had found her under the root of an old oak stump not far from the house. Halvor fairly flew home and came into the house all out of breath.

"Father, is it true that you have found a baby girl?"

"Hush, you mustn't make any noise. Mother is sick."

Halvor quieted down at once. Everything seemed strange in the house. Over in the corner lay his mother, pale and weak; and over by the stove sat her mother, old Mrs. Sandbakken, with a bundle in her lap.

"Come here, Halvor, and see your little sister."

Halvor grew fond of her at once—more fond than he had ever been of anything in the world. He asked if she was alive, but needed no answer for at that moment she uttered a cry that made him jump. She was the prettiest thing he had ever seen. And to think that they had found her under a stump! That was the most interesting thing of all. How awkward it was that his mother should be sick just now when her help was needed to take care of the baby.

"I wonder," thought he, "if there are any more to be found?" He got a spade and began quietly to dig under an oak stump near the barn. Finding nothing, he concluded that he would have to be content with the one they found.

When the mother was up and around again, he had to watch his chance when she was out to go to the cradle and look at his little sister. What fun it was to put his index finger into her little hand and feel her tiny fingers grasp it and hold it fast. And when she held up one little foot, how he loved to take one toe at a time and say what he had learned from the Kjeldalen children: "This one stole, this one carried away, this one broke the lock, this one tattled, and this one got all the blame."

It was not until late in the fall that the little one could be baptized, for the congregation had no regular pastor but had to get along with a few visits each year from Pastors Preus, Ottesen, or Brandt, or some other of the untiring pioneer pastors who with almost unheard-of courage and under conditions of unbelievable difficulties and hardships, traveled from place to place in the woods, organizing congregations and reminding the pioneers that the domain of the God they had worshipped in Norway extended even here. These men, Koren, Larsen, Stub, Ottesen, Brandt, Muus, and others have done our people a service whose value can never be measured. They suffered like good soldiers, and they brought light and happiness to the humble small homes scattered far and wide.

Søren and Anne's girl was all of four months old when Klemmetsrud dropped in one evening and told them that Pastor Brandt was to conduct services the next Sunday in the school house. Since so long a time had passed since the child's birth, the parents had ample time to disagree about the name. At last it was decided that she should be named for Søren's mother whose name was Guri.

She was therefore called Jenny because Jenny was considered much finer than Guri.

The day Jenny was christened was a red-letter day for Halvor. He went to church and although he was only seven years old the sermon made such an impression on him that he was not himself for months. It was about the Judgment Day. So vividly was this day pictured that he thought he saw the whole world on fire and heard the shrieks of the doomed as they were thrown into outer darkness. "And," said the preacher, "it is coming. It is coming soon. We are living in the last days." He repeated this several times. By "soon" Halvor thought, of course, he meant in a day or two. It did not occur to him to doubt the pastor's word. Nor could he imagine that by this the minister could mean anything except a week or two at the most. And he was terribly frightened.

He also recalled something he had heard his godmother, Gunhild Knudson, read from a little book which was to her a very dear devotional book, and quite as reliable as the Bible itself. It told of a young girl who had been transported to the place of torment. There she had seen great numbers of the damned in a huge kettle of boiling water. They stretched up their arms and sometimes succeeded in getting ahold of the rim of the kettle and tried to pull themselves out. But then the Evil One himself went around with a red hot poker which he passed around the rim, so that they had to drop their hold. The book also told that some of these doomed ones were not more than seven years old, judging by the size of their hands. From this Halvor deduced that those who were under seven were safe. Unfortunately he was over seven, and he had often whistled, walked backwards, and whittled on Sunday, and sinned in other ways. He felt sure, however, that his father would be able to take care of him if the Day would only come when they were together. But what if it should come when his father was away or he himself was in school. The very thought made him sick. It was all his parents could do to make him go to school. He secured a seat near the window so that he could look out every once in a while to see if there were any signs of the approaching Doom. He imagined it would come like a storm, and he decided that the moment he saw anything that looked ominous he would make a dash for home in spite of anything the teacher could say or do, so that he could be with his father and mother, and the little sister who at least was sure to get to Heaven. In a pinch he might even hang on to her and thus get to the same place as she. Strangely enough one day after another passed by, and the Judgment Day never came. Several times things looked bad, and Halvor grew pale and asked his father if the world was going to end. But nothing came of it. At last the boy began to have secret doubts about the pastor's reliability. Little by little, however, he stopped watching the sky for signs of the coming of the great storm.

Later Halvor came to be very fond of Pastor Brandt. It chanced the next spring that the pastor who was making another tour through these parts walked past the house and saw Halvor up in a tree investigating a bird's nest. He called up to him to ask if there was a path leading through the woods to Klemmetsrud's. The boy answered that he did not know what a "path" was. "Oh," explained the minister, "I mean a way, a road." Of course, Halvor could show him one. He got down from the tree and walked along with him through the woods a short distance. Pastor Brandt asked him if he could read Norwegian. "No, not Norwegian, but English," answered the boy.

When they parted the minister took a Norwegian A-B-C book out of his pocket and gave it to Halvor. And the next day he sent him by a neighbor's daughter, who was in the confirmation class, a Catechism, and an Explanation, and a Bible History. The boy grew to love these books and went to work to learn to read them as if his life depended upon it.

As he could speak Norwegian—of a kind—and could read English, he made such rapid progress that in a trice he had learned to read them. One evening while mother sat milking, Halvor stood rattling off something he had learned by heart. Before he knew what had happened the book had fallen into the water trough. The blue back binding loosened and curled up. Halvor cried and begged his mother not to tell Pastor Brandt how badly he had treated the beautiful book.

A Bit of History

It was the Fourth of July, 1863, that the announcement was made throughout the land that General Meade had won a great victory in the bloody battle of Gettysburg; and at the same time came the news from the South that Grant had taken Vicksburg. The government needed new men to take the places of the fallen. A huge army was to be raised so as to give the brave and desperate Rebels the crushing defeat that was needed to end the war.

These events of world history became a part of little Halvor's life. Now his father refused to stay at home any longer. He must take a hand in the bloody game. He came home one night accompanied by an elderly man who had lately come from Norway. After having eaten his supper in silence Søren said calmly and firmly, "Well, now, Anne, I am going to do as I please. This man, Amund Bø, is to stay here and help you run the farm because I am going to the war. All the rest have and I can't stand the disgrace of staying at home." This settled the matter. Anne had to get his clothes out and put them in order, and in a few days everything was arranged.

Søren said goodbye to Anne in a thick voice and admonished her to take good care of the farm until he came back. Then he kissed the baby in the cradle and turned to go. At this Anne began to carry on. She had a premonition that Søren would never come back alive. "Why, of course, I'll be back. You shall see that with the help of God I'll be back. Now, be good to Halvor while I am gone." And with that he was off.

Halvor had permission to go with him as far as Kjeldalen's, for Søren was to drive with him to town. At first the boy had insisted that he was going to war with him. But as that was impossible he had to be satisfied with going just that little way. Then came the parting. Søren could hardly utter a word. He took the boy in his arms and forced himself to say, "Now you must be a good boy and mind your mother. And you must not forget your father, but pray to God that he may come back to you." Then he and Ole climbed up into the wagon and drove off. Halvor watched them until they had passed the turn in the road; then he lay down prone on the ground and wept as he had never wept before.

Søren went at once to Green Bay where he enlisted and from there he was sent south at once. He was away from home for two years, and during this time poor little Halvor was almost completely neglected. His mother always thought he was in the way, and small as he was, he had to work all day long with Amund Bø, who was his only companion. The old fellow hardly ever spoke. In this he was wise, as he had nothing to say. He would go along all day working with the boy without uttering anything except monosyllabic replies to the boy's questions. His one and only interest was to save his wages; his only luxury was chewing tobacco. This he cut up into small cubes which he would thread around, so as to make them last longer. Halvor often asked him about the war, but Amund knew nothing.

Nevertheless, a companionship of a sort sprang up between them. Halvor looked up to the old man as to one who possessed unfathomable wisdom if he would only impart it. They slept together up in the loft and Amund took care not to wake the boy when he got up early. But sometimes Halvor was already awake, and then he would ask, "Say Amund, where do you think father is now?" This was the one thing he was thinking and dreaming about.

What in the world was war for? He had heard that they shot at one another. Who could tell but what they had shot and killed his father. He wept bitterly.

And how hard it was to have to work from morning until evening while the other boys were in school getting ahead of him, he who had been the smartest. He was so tired that he longed for Sundays, for then he might at least rest—or for rainy mornings when it was not necessary to get up so early as usual. Then he might lie up under the roof listening to the rain pattering over his head. And there is something wonderfully pleasant about this sound. It was his greatest pleasure except on the few occasions when his mother was outdoors and he indoors when he could play with his little sister and tell her about Father.

Letters from Søren were few and far between. They told only where he was, and that he was well. Money was always enclosed.

There were only a few men left in the settlement at this time. Thrond Knudson was at home, for he was lame and could not be accepted as a soldier. Klemmetsrud was afraid he would besmirch his soul by associating with so many wicked people, so he hired a substitute. He believed he could do more good by remaining at home and comforting the many wives who were in constant fear of receiving a message that their husbands had fallen. The war was the only subject of conversation among people. But it was little news they received, so far out in the country. They went about in suspense, suffering intensely. Reliable news came to the effect that Knud Hansen, who had gone to war with Søren, had been killed in battle. A short time later they heard that Østen Børthe had fared the same way. Then Halvor Kjeldalen came home minus one eye. He brought the news that his brother Hans was starving in the prison at Andersonville. A little later Ole Findreng came home sick. He went around drinking and visiting the homes of men who were at war, feeling sure of being treated to a drink there. He came to visit Anne, too. He could not, to be sure, tell her anything about her husband, but he did tell the most hair-raising stories of the horrors of war. He himself had killed at least a thousand Rebels. Little Halvor sat listening with open mouth, and he decided that Ole was a greater man than even Pastor Brandt.

In the spring of 1865 Halvor was allowed to attend school a day now and then when there was not too much to do at home. There one day in April he heard that the war was over. A little later he heard a man who had just come from town tell the teacher that President Lincoln had been assassinated. Soldiers then began coming home in great numbers, and wherever one went one saw the blue uniform. The whole town was rife with tales of war. Everyone was talking about battles, and General Grant, and the assassination of Lincoln. A peddler went to every home selling a miserable portrait of General Grant and a still more trashy picture representing the assassination of Lincoln. There sat the president, his wife, and other friends in Ford's Theater in Washington, while John Wilkes Booth stood behind him holding a revolver to his head. This was considered a masterpiece of pictorial art and was framed and hung on the wall to be gazed at and admired. And they sang a sad ballad which some rhymester or other had written for *Emigranten* and which proved to be a song hit. It began thus:

O land, O land, what must thou see
Of bloodshed and disloyalty.
Perjurers with lust for blood
Have brought on Thee, of woe, a flood.

In atrocities the Rebels engaged
Like boar with foaming mouth they raged.
The arch-scoundrel finally ran away
Like an ogre he hid from light of Day.

The ballad further relates how John Wilkes Booth, "the murderer blind left his wife so good and kind," when the devil had incited him to murder the President:

The devil nudged and egged him on
Told him to be brave and strong.
To go to Ford's he did him tell
There to do his deed so fell.

For thirteen days he fled in fear
Afraid like Cain his doom to hear.
Shot like a wolf, he fell with thud
O Maryland, thou drank'st his blood.

The poem then ended with the following unmotivated prayer:

Look, O God, in mercy kind
Upon our land, that peace we find.
Help us, Lord to live with merit,
That heaven at last we may inherit.

Halvor, too, learned this song and firmly believed it to be the grandest poem ever written, although it puzzled him somewhat how anyone could know exactly what the devil said to Booth, since the ballad said expressly that the two were alone during their conversation.

Presently Anne began to say that it was certainly strange that Søren did not return now that the war was over. There came a letter saying that she might soon expect him. Halvor longed for him so intensely that he cried every night because his father had not appeared. Then, one morning, when he came down from the loft, he saw a soldier's uniform on the bench near the table, and in the bed lay Father just as he used to look. Halvor seemed dimly to remember having dreamed that a man had come up to the loft with a light in his hand and had looked at him and stroked his cheek. Now he rushed to the bed and threw himself upon his father.

"You must not wake Father. He is tired," said Anne, who just then came in. But Søren was already awake. He sat up, took Halvor in his arms, looked at him and said, "Why, how freckled you have got! Hand me my pants, my boy." Never before had Halvor been so happy. He stood at his father's side like a faithful dog and listened to every word he said. Søren was the same as before, and talked very little about his experiences. He was a little thinner, but straight and strong; and the faithful gray eyes had the same friendly glow, and the voice the same ring. Halvor thought it strange that he of all others should have a father who was so much handsomer, and kinder, and wiser than other men; but he had to be satisfied with the simple fact that such was the case. They were as good friends as ever; and the sun shone more clearly, the fields were greener, and the birds sang more sweetly than they ever had done while his father was away.

The Congregation Gets a Church and a Pastor

Søren had no reason to complain. Anne had managed the farm very well in his absence and everything was in a good condition. He went to work at once, and could not see that he had lost anything by his service to his country.

During the first few years after the war, times were, as most people know, very good. The farmers got between two and three dollars for a bushel of wheat, twenty cents a pound for pork, and proportionate prices for other farm products. But then everything one needed to buy was also dear, so one was nothing ahead. Most people, however, did not realize this. They knew only that their pockets were full of money and they spent it royally. But those who were careful and sensible laid the foundation for substantial fortunes.

Among the farmers of Springville great changes took place within a couple of years. They exchanged their oxen for horses, and in place of their first rude cabins they built good and often large and commodious frame houses. The woods were cleared and burned, the roads were improved, and the congregation erected a beautiful church.

It was Søren Helgeson who took the lead in this project. First subscribing a handsome sum himself, he went around soliciting contributions until three thousand dollars had been raised. Then materials were bought and the church was built by Ole Kjeldalen.

In a surprisingly short time it stood all completed in the center of the churchyard on the hill. There was not even a dispute about its location since the churchyard had already been laid out. Thus the reef upon which so many congregations have stranded was cleared without any mishap.

It was almost pathetic how proud people were of their new church. The day when Pastors Preus and Mikkelsen came and dedicated it was for many the greatest day in their lives. Søren Helgeson made use of the occasion to have a housewarming in the new home which had been completed simultaneously with the church, and both pastors were his guests for the night. Pastor Preus took particular notice of little Halvor and thought him a bright little fellow. He asked him what he intended to be when he grew up. Halvor did not know but rather thought he wanted to be a carpenter. Then Pastor Preus spoke of the school in Decorah and asked Søren if he would not like to send the boy there. Søren answered in the affirmative but thought there was no hurry to decide about the matter until after the boy was confirmed.

The day after the dedication a business meeting of the congregation was held in the church. Bethel congregation had met to take up the matter of calling a regular minister without delay. There was a large attendance and all were heartily in favor of calling a pastor. But who should it be? No one in the congregation knew of anyone who was to be had. An older minister would, they feared, be too expensive. It would be best if the Reverend Mr. Preus would find someone for them, preferably a young unmarried man who would be able to get along on a small salary. Thrond Knudson opined that if the congregation would only call a minister the government would support him or at least buy a parsonage for him. But when Pastor Preus explained that the minister would, of course, have to be supported by voluntary contributions from the members of the congregation, Thrond grew thoughtful. He would, of course, pay his share, but he wondered what Pastor Harbitz would have thought of such an arrangement.

Klemmetsrud did not know if they could afford to hire a minister. And besides, there were in the congregation a couple of men who had a gift for witnessing for the Lord. Surely these gifts should be made use of. He finally agreed, however, to join in the calling of an "organized" minister if they could be sure to find one who was really converted. For such a man would not ask about the salary, but work because he felt a call to do so and was impelled by the Spirit. And for that matter, Klemmetsrud thought it was too bad they could never have a congregational meeting without always talking about money. And with a deep sigh he sat down.

Søren Helgeson retorted that he did not think Klemmetsrud should complain as he had certainly not contributed more than he could afford. If they wanted a minister, Søren maintained, they must pay him so that he could live; and this they could certainly afford to do. A small fraction of what was spent in the saloons each year would keep the minister in luxury.

The final outcome was that on the Reverend Mr. Preus' advice they decided to call Pastor Evensen.[4] He had studied in St. Louis, had been in the army a couple of years, and was still young and unmarried. To decide what salary to offer him took considerable time. As he was to serve two other small congregations which would, of course, contribute a little, Klemmetsrud thought that two hundred dollars a year would be plenty. But after some jangling it was finally decided that Bethel congregation would promise its pastor four hundred dollars a year besides festival offerings and incidentals. It was settled that he was to live at Helgeson's until a parsonage could be built; for he was said to be engaged to be married. It was said, too, that his betrothed had money, a fact that gave some of his future parishioners the idea that it would be possible to cut his salary at some later time.

With this selection of a pastor, Thrond was very much pleased. Pastor Evensen was a Valdris. And as Thrond limped his way home he told everyone that he knew the new minister's relatives in Norway. They were from Vang, he said, and were very fine people. They had come to America about twenty years ago, more or less. He also knew all about the minister himself. "It's him as wrote the Gospel about the Pharisee and the Republican. And the first time I read it I says to my wife, 'Gunhild, says I, Gunhild, a Valdris has wrote that,' says I."

Klemmetsrud was less satisfied with the choice of a minister. He would have preferred that they had called Andrewson, or some other minister who one could sure had undergone a true conversion. And his friend Hatlevik-Ole, too, thought they could have made a better choice. Ole was somewhat given to going on sprees, which he freely admitted, consoling himself, however, with the fact that there was not a word in the Bible which he could not spell. He was, moreover, particularly fond of Linderot's Book of Sermons, the only book he possessed. Linderot was hard, he said, but he would not sell that book for a hundred dollars. He, like Klemmetsrud, had little faith in the *stas* ministers in the Norwegian Synod. "They can," he said, "take Preus and Professor Larsen, and old Stub, and Otteson from Kaskeland[5] and as many more as they like of the ministers of the Norwegian Synod, and I'll put Andrewson up against the whole bunch and bet a horse on him."

But Klemmetsrud and his followers were few. It was Aanun Strand who voiced the sentiments of the majority when he said that the most important thing in calling a minister was to get one who stood by the "pure, correct, Lutheran alphabet."

The Reverend Mr. Evensen accepted the call which was tendered him and arrived almost immediately in Springville with all his goods. This was no great wealth—only a trunk full of clothes and a box of books. Søren Helgeson met him in town and brought him, and his trunk, and his box, home. Søren's new house stood on a little knoll on the south side of the road. In the main wing which stood with the gable to the road was the living room with a door leading to a bedroom which was called "the chamber" and was used only as a guest room. From it, stairs led to the second floor on which were three bedrooms. In the wing to the west there were a kitchen which also served as dining room, a large family bedroom, and a pantry. In front of this wing there was a veranda with fancy wooden grill work. The old house which stood farther back from the road was now a granary. Still farther back were the horse barn and the cow barn. At one side of the house was a garden with apple trees and long rows of currant and gooseberry bushes.

The largest room upstairs, the one with the view to the road, was made ready for the minister, and it was here he spent the first days after his arrival preparing the installation sermon on which so much would depend. He knew that it would be discussed and picked to pieces; and he struggled hard with it, writing and erasing and writing again until far into the night.

When Sunday arrived, everyone was out early. It was not to be wondered at that all the parishioners were curious to see the new minister, for he was the first one they could really call their own. They stood out in the churchyard waiting for him to arrive. Thrond Knudson was speculating as to whether he who knew the minister's relatives in Norway ought not to be the first to go and shake hands with him and tell him that he had read the Gospel of the Pharisee and the Republican and that he knew at once that a Valdris must have written it.

At last Søren arrived driving his handsome team and light buggy. And in the seat with him sat the minister; he appeared to be a little self-conscious from knowing that he was the object of several hundred eyes. At the gate he jumped out of the buggy, and one could get a better look at him. All agreed that he did not look particularly distinguished. He was tall, thin, blond, and smoothly shaven; and his threadbare, greenish-black clothes did not fit very well. He greeted them with a hasty "Good Morning" and satchel in hand, made his way into the sacristy. Then everyone streamed into the church and took seats, the men on the right side and the women on the left. Old Hatlevik was more solemn than usual when, after having been in consultation with the minister in the vestry, he came out directly behind him and proceeded to read the opening prayer. And he hemmed and hawed vehemently before he succeeded in uttering the words, "As our opening hymn we shall sing hymn number five; and I wish to ask someone in the congregation to start it as I have such a bad cold."

But when the minister came out to chant the collect and the epistle, a very awkward situation arose. Hatlevik-Ole, as parish clerk, made ready to sing, "And with thy spirit." But the minister could not sing. He just read the ritual; and so Hatlevik-Ole could, of course, not sing the responses as he usually did either. It was most embarrassing. Thrond was ready to sink to the floor. And to think how Pastor Harbitz could sing! And this poor fellow could not chant even the least bit. And there were many who thought it very strange that one who was a minister was unable to sing.

When the Reverend Mr. Evensen entered the pulpit he was also ill at ease. He looked with a pleading glance at the congregation. There sat the men, some of them in shirtsleeves, turning their chewing tobacco in their cheeks as they stared at him. Many of the women had tears in their eyes, so moved were they by the solemnity of the occasion. On the front bench sat a row of them nursing their babies while others were trying to stop the cries of theirs by forcing them to drink milk from bottles brought from home. The young folks giggled down by the door and up in the gallery.

When the minister had progressed a ways into his sermon his courage returned. He said he had not come to bring them words of worldly wisdom, but the simple Gospel of the cross. Life was, he said, dreadfully sad and absolutely meaningless if one had nothing more to look forward to than a few years of toil and care and then a death without hope. It was only the Christian faith that could give life a meaning. And he asked their forbearance. One had no right, he said, to demand of a man who had only one or two talents that he should produce interest from five or ten, but only that he should use faithfully those that he had. That he would earnestly try to do. He would not try to please everyone, but confine himself to sincerely striving to please Him who had taken him into His hire. He wished, he said, to be treated like one of the congregation and to share their joys and sorrows. He did not pretend to be more than a beggar at the door of grace—one who had been called to lead a group of such beggars asking for the bread of life. Thrond felt greatly relieved. And it was Aanun Strand who again voiced the general opinion when at the close of the services he stood in the churchyard, took a new chew of tobacco and said, "He's a corking good preacher just the same!"

The American Saloon

During the first flush years after the Civil War there was a great deal of drinking and carousing in the Springville settlement. Now that the farmers had horses it was so easy to make a flying trip to town, and they had money. Those who had been to war had to drink to regain their strength after the hardships they had endured. Surely no one could begrudge them anything. They had risked their lives for their country and felt that now they might do as they pleased. Those who had remained at home needed something to refresh them after the long period of monotonous toil on the farms. What good did their money do them if they were not allowed to spend it for cheer when they went to town?

When they had sold their wheat or their pork, they would gather in Myran's saloon where it was always nice and warm. There was always someone who wanted to treat. And then, of course, the others had to show that they could afford to do the same. If no one else cared to treat, Myran did so himself. He was a great big burly fellow and exceptionally kind hearted. How he would laugh at the comical war yarns and swear that the narrators were great fellows and pass drinks in their honor. One could always borrow a fiver from him for a few days. Many were the horses standing freezing in front of his place of business in winter. If a steady customer was seen making as if to leave after watering his horses, Myran always came to the door and said, "Well, well, Ole, have you got too stuck-up to come in?" Then, of course, Ole had to go in and take at least one drink to show that he was a good sport, and then another, and another, and another, and something in his bottle for the trip home. And how the farmers raced their horses on the way home! Little Halvor often sat on the steps of his house during an evening listening to their hoarse shouting and cursing as they lashed their horses in their efforts to pass each other. How glad he was that his father never came home drunk.

Søren never went in to Myran's except to find a neighbor and induce him to go home. As was natural, Myran disliked him. Søren imagined, said Myran, that he was better than the rest, but he, Myran, could well remember the time that the big-bug did not own more than the clothes on his back; and if he thought he could be elected county treasurer with Myran against him, he had another guess coming.

Ole Findreng, poor fellow, was one of Myran's very best customers. He had always been a happy-go-lucky soul who was ready for anything that might turn up. If there was a barn raising, Ole was the first man there. Liquor was always served at these gatherings. What fun they had seeing who could tell the tallest story and who was the strongest, with a fight as the usual outcome. Then in the fall there were husking bees, and it would not occur to anyone not to invite Ole. At these bees the guests worked hard until late; then there was a good meal followed by a merry night of drinking, dancing, and boisterousness. Ole took a pride in working as hard as anyone as long as the work lasted; for this reason the young people saw to it that he got his share of liquor, and then some. But of late, since he had been accused of stealing, he had become shy and morose, and had started to drink worse than ever; the only difference was that now he did his drinking at home and on the sly. When he came back from the war ragged and miserable he began again where he had left off. For was he not now a hero who had suffered to save his country?

He lived in a miserable hut on the low land just below Søren Helgeson's house. How his sickly and foolish wife had managed while he was gone no one knew. She had a nest full of young ones and was unable to work. But it certainly did not help matters to have her husband come back from the war. He had his ups and downs, at times being drunk, and at others only half drunk. He wept profusely whenever he talked about what a shame it was for one who had risked his life for his country to be in want. The only friend he had was Myran. He was in perfect agreement with Ole that his war services had not been rewarded as one had a right to expect, and to console him he loaned him money occasionally or filled his empty jug. One would have to search long to find so kind a man as Myran.

Pastor Evensen took up his work with zeal and energy. He was not lazy. He went about calling on people and learning to know their living conditions. He could not help seeing how many of them were too fond of strong drink. He called on them, one after the other, and warned them against drunkenness. He also preached against it in such a way that it struck home and offended many. It chanced one day that the minister came walking past Ole Findreng's miserable hut. Out by the wall stood the wife crying, and over by the cow barn a strange man was walking around. The pastor asked the wife what the matter was and learned that the man had come to fetch their only cow which Ole had put in hock to Myran. Friend Myran had taken everything else, and now he was taking the cow too. The woman wiped her eyes and sobbed out that she could not see how she and her children were going to get through the winter without a cow. If they could only have kept this cow they would not suffer because a neighbor had promised to give them some sacks of flour and let the oldest boy work it out. As for clothes they could manage with their old rags, and they could stay indoors when it was cold.

Knowing that the husband not only drank up what little he earned but abused his wife and children besides, Pastor Evensen was interested in knowing what her opinion was of such a husband, and he intimated something about her marriage being an unfortunate one. Her reply was the most touching thing he had ever heard. "Ole is," she said, "a real kind man. He is a little too fond of drink, poor fellow; but otherwise he is as good a man as is to be found."

Ole chanced to come home just then and was sober. Pastor Evensen spoke to him long and earnestly, and the poor man promised that he would never taste another drop. His wife believed what he said and was as happy as if he had not made and broken innumerable such promises before. Yes, indeed, women are just so credulous. How foolish they are, yet what a blessing it is that such is the case—that they are simple enough to believe in their husbands and love them even if they are such men as no one with a grain of sense would have the least respect for. A man cannot be so brainless. Suppose the case were reversed, and that it was the wife who drank and wallowed in filth and neglected her home and wasted the money and came home nights smelling disgustedly of whiskey and tobacco and stormed and swore. There would certainly be more divorces if such were the case. There is hardly a man in all the world who would be senseless enough to endure such a state of affairs, or strong enough to bear it. But the women! They suffer and weep and love and console themselves with the thought that there are no saloons in heaven.

To make the story short, the happiness of Ole Findreng's wife was destined to be short lived this time too. A few days later Ole had an important errand in town.

"For God's sake be careful now, Ole," said his wife.

"Sure," answered Ole. He caught a ride with Søren who promised himself that he would see to it that the poor fellow did not go in to Myran's.

When they were all through with their business and were ready to start for home, Myran came over to see them.

"Hello! And how is everything? I suppose you're too stuck-up to take a drink today, Søren."

"Yes, you're right. I really feel above that."

"Well how about you, Ole? You haven't got so proud, have you?"

"Oh, no, it isn't that; but I didn't intend to have a drink today. I can't afford it."

"Oh, pshaw! I was intending to treat you anyway. And Danielson is inside." Ole and Danielson had been comrades in the war. So, of course, Ole wanted to go in for just a minute, not to drink, just to talk to Danielson a little.

"No. You're going home with me," said Søren. He was in dead earnest and was growing desperate.

"Oh-ho!" said Myran, laughing heartily. "So you've had a guardian appointed, eh?" Of course Ole could not stand that. He simply had to show that he was his own boss and that he was not afraid like Søren.

Søren grew angry. "You are right. I am afraid of whiskey. But I am not afraid of Myran." He walked up to him and without mincing told him what a damned scoundrel he was. People streamed out of the saloon, drunk and sober alike, to see what it was all about. They egged the two on, and the result was that Søren gave Myran such a thrashing that he begged for peace. Then Søren went to the justice of the peace, reported what had happened, and offered to pay any fine that was demanded. Then he went back to the saloon to see how Myran was getting along. He found him seated in a circle of friends cursing Søren and, with the help of said friends, verbally killing him. Myran had just treated the whole crowd, Ole Findreng with the rest. Under these particular circumstances Ole could hardly refuse to take a drink with his maltreated friend. How good it tasted to get a little whiskey inside of him after two days of abstinence. Now he refused absolutely to go home with Søren. He could get home by himself. Søren took him by the collar and tried to drag him out to the wagon. A number of his friends came to his rescue. Søren asked if there was anyone else who wanted a thrashing. At that pandemonium broke loose. They would not stand for this. This was a free country, and if Ole did not want to go home he didn't have to.

There were too many of them for Søren, and he was thrown out. He stood thinking for a moment. There was, however, nothing more he could do. He had to go home alone. On the way home he sat boiling with indignation, and it occurred to him that it might not be a bad idea next time he went to town to go in to Myran's and take a few drinks, just enough to get reckless on, and then get busy and clean up the whole place. When he got home and had put up his horses, he went into the house and tried to explain how his clothes had got so torn. And, of course, Anne whimpered and carried on over his having been in a fight. And to have such a thing happen just now when the minister was staying with them! She knew that the end would be that Søren would turn out to be a common brawler and that she might expect to hear at any time that he had been killed.

Weary and exasperated, Søren went straight up to the minister's room and told him what had happened and declared that he was not ashamed of what he had done. Then he took a bag of candy for the Findreng children and went down to break the news of Ole's backsliding as gently as possible to the wife. She thanked him and wept.

When Ole came home staggering the next night, he was drunk and in a sorry state. He took turns blubbering and scolding. He was angry at his wife because she was, he said, going to have another baby. "And Lord knows we have more than enough to bother with now." Finally he fell in a heap and his wife helped him to bed. During the latter part of the night he got up and went out. His wife lay waiting for him to come back and when considerable time had passed she grew frightened. She went out and called him but got no answer. Then she ran up to Søren's house and asked Søren to go back with her. She did not dare go and look but she thought Ole had gone in the cow barn. She was right. When Søren entered the barn he found Ole. He had at last done what he had so often threatened. He had hanged himself.

Søren almost had to carry the wife into the house. Then he persuaded her and the children to go home with him. In the morning he got Thrond to go with him and they quietly buried Ole. So ended Ole Findreng's saga. The event made a deep impression upon everyone in the community. The children were frightened when his name was mentioned. Halvor could not get the tragedy out of his mind. His godmother, Gunhild Knudson, had impressed upon him with as much emphasis as if it were a main tenet of the Christian faith that for a suicide there is no hope.

A day or two later when Søren was in town he met Myran and asked him if he had heard what had happened to Ole. "No. Nothing bad, I hope."

"Oh no. Nothing worth mentioning," said Søren, dryly. "He has hanged himself. That's all."

This news gave Myran such a shock that he forgot all about his original intention of giving Søren a beating as he had bragged that he would do. He had, instead, to run in and get a drink to brace himself up. It was only by the skin of his teeth that he escaped the uncomfortable feeling of discovering that he had such a thing as a conscience. But, shucks! It wasn't his fault. He had never forced Ole to drink. It was rather lucky for him, he reflected, that this happened just now when Ole did not owe him more than a dollar or two. He would be magnanimous and let the widow off from paying this debt.

Ministerial Timber

The year that they lived in the same house brought much pleasure and benefit to both Pastor Evensen and Søren. Since Søren knew everyone in the congregation, the minister consulted him in everything and found in him a good helper. He could not help seeing that Søren was a man on whom he could depend. They became bosom friends and many a night they sat up until the cock crew, talking and planning how to reform the congregation.

The Reverend Mr. Evensen had studied many things besides theology, and he enjoyed imparting to Søren odds and ends of secular and church history in order to widen his horizon. He had made a special study of Norwegian history, and Søren now heard for the first time of Harald the Fairhaired, Haakon the Good, Egil Skalagrimson, Saint Olaf, and other heroes of Norway's golden age. There were many in the congregation who did not like it that Søren and the minister were so inseparable. Søren was certainly no better than the rest, they thought. Perhaps he thought he was supporting the minister all alone. Well, he would get a piece of their mind the next time he came around to collect the minister's salary.

Things certainly did go too far. Pastor Evensen liked to go along with Søren when he was doing his work on the farm. He enjoyed seeing his great dexterity. Sometimes he could not refrain from taking hold himself just for the fun of it. Passers-by were likely to see the pastor helping Søren fell a tree or break a colt. To tell the truth, here were sown the first seeds of dissension in the congregation.

Our young friend, Halvor, enjoyed his association with the minister quite as much as did his father. During the two years since his father's return from the war, Halvor had a happy time of it. When school was not in session he, of course, had to help his father with the heavy work on the farm; but it was really only fun because he was with his father and they passed the time most interestingly by asking and answering questions about the war. Halvor at least never tired of this pastime.

He had become unusually clever and handy. He could drive the old horses quite as well as his father, and he felt sure he could handle the young skittish ones which his father had just purchased if he had only been permitted to try. In winter, when wheat or pork was to be hauled to town, Halvor had to drive a load occasionally. He did not find it particularly exciting to sit bumping along hour after hour, freezing and clucking to the horses, with no other company except some dead hogs.

Three months in the winter and the same number of months in the summer the boy attended school. Occasionally he, like other boys, needed to be punished, either by a few blows across his hand or, what was much worse, by being made to stay in at recess. For the very gravest offenses, a boy might be compelled to sit with a girl. Things never went that far with Halvor. He saw to it that he escaped that disgrace.

But my! Oh my! What fun it was to go to school, taking it all in all—especially in the summer. Then he went barefoot, and that made it easier to dress. All he had to put on was blue overalls, a striped shirt, and one suspender. He preferred wearing only one as it was easier.

In winter, too, school was enjoyable for then the big boys attended, and occasionally there was a fight among them—usually over a girl. When rivalry grew too bitter, one would challenge the other to fight it out. Having first made a ring in the snow the combatants each took a position within it, and with thick sheepskin mitts on their hands they rushed at each other until one or the other landed outside of the ring. Halvor enjoyed watching this sport and occasionally tried it with Jimmy Mott or some other Yankee boy who made fun of him because he was Norwegian and had white hair.

Of all the boys in the school Halvor was farther advanced for his age. He had spelled down the school several times. And on the last day of the winter term many of the parents were present to hear their children speak pieces and to rejoice over the prizes they received. Søren was really proud of his boy. For Halvor not only won prizes in reading and arithmetic, but an extra award for diligence. Even Anne secretly thought it was fine but said only that she was afraid the boy would become a smart aleck.

In the midst of all these victories, however, Halvor suffered a crushing blow—one which made him weary of life and caused him to speculate as to whether he should not leave home and go to a new world somewhere, win a great kingdom, and come back and ravage America with fire and sword and destroy the Christian religion. He had fallen in love with a lovely ten-year-old Yankee girl with brown eyes, a cute little nose, and long curly hair. She had never actually given him reason to hope, but yet she had smiled at him several times and he could not help but love her. A Norwegian girl could never be so beautiful as she.

Halvor thought about her early and late, and his heart was sick with love. He thought, of course, that she returned his affection. And then one day—it was many years before he could think of it without a piercing pain—she said to him, "I like Jimmy Mott better than I like you." It hurt cruelly. If it had only been some other boy! But Jimmy Mott—a dunce who was way behind Halvor in his studies and who had red hair and sore eyes! It was so humiliating that it was enough to drive one mad. The next time he fought

Jimmy, he did not stop until both of them lay on their backs gasping for breath. For homely as Jimmy was, he was, nevertheless, tough and strong.

Halvor now became a misogynist. No more would he look at those miserable girls. His heart was, indeed, broken all to smithereens; but he would bear his pain in silence. No one should know of his sufferings, least of all the faithless Fanny who actually was capable of loving such a boy as Jimmy Mott.

Pastor Evensen and Halvor had become great friends. The boy was, in the pastor's opinion, a bright youngster and very much advanced in his studies for one of his age. The two often took long walks together or sat and talked in the study. This was Halvor's happiest time. He received instruction in Norwegian and even a little in German, and dipped into the realms of history and religion as well; and he firmly believed that no one so kind or so learned as Pastor Evenson had ever lived. How he longed to be like him! "It must be great," he thought, "to be the most important person at all gatherings and always to be seated at the head of the table and treated to the best of everything and not be a bit bashful. And then to be able to stand and talk to so many people every Sunday!" And the boy often recalled what Pastor Preus had said about the school in Decorah. He believed he would beg his father to send him there.

When Søren and the minister sat talking way into the night, Halvor would insist on sitting up listening to them. No matter what the clock said, he would assure them that he was not the least bit sleepy. It soon began to be the subject of conversation throughout the community that that boy of Søren Helgesen's was going to be sent to study for the ministry as soon as he was confirmed. Søren, too, thought the thing was quite possible although it would be hard to send the boy away for such a long time.

Then one Sunday something happened which settled the matter once for all. It raised Halvor very high in the estimation of the more serious minded of the congregation, and they agreed that it would be a sin and a shame if Søren, who was blessed with such a son and could well afford to educate him, did not let him study for the ministry.

This incident happened in church on a Sunday when the weather was oppressively hot. Halvor sat squeezed in between his father and another man and suffered intensely. It was so roasting hot and so muggy, and he needed so desperately to scratch his back, but could not get to do so, squeezed in as he was. The minister seemed never to get through with his sermon. At last the boy's suffering became so great that his patience gave out completely. He began to cry, and then at last he was allowed to go out.

"What were you crying for in church today, Halvor?" asked Knud, the son of Gunhild and Thrond, on the way home from church. Gunhild's indignation was instantly kindled. She, who had received Halvor when he came into the world and had carried him when he was baptized and who had such a high opinion of both his and his father's learning—she did not need to be told why Halvor was crying. "You should be ashamed to ask such a question, Knud," she said. "That boy, small as he is, has more understanding of the Word of God than most grown-ups. You might thank your God, big overgrown lummox that you are, if you knew half as much about religion as that boy does!"

Thrond was of the same opinion. His respect for Halvor increased tremendously. He thought it was almost uncanny that the lad knew so much. "Who knows but what he will some day be a second Pastor Harbitz? Well, who knows?" The only thing that worried him was that Halvor's neck was rather short to wear the ruff.

Gunhild often told about this incident. Soon it was rumored everywhere that Søren's Halvor had been so moved by Pastor Evensen's sermon on the destruction of Jerusalem that he had sobbed and had to leave the church in order not to faint. Would you believe it? That boy had comprehended the message so thoroughly and taken it so to heart—that twelve-year-old boy—although Klemmetsrud who was usually so easily moved had sat dry-eyed through it all and had failed to grasp the seriousness of the sermon! Klemmetsrud himself admitted that there might be something to all this, and he could only express the hope that Halvor might be the means of bringing his parents to think seriously of the welfare of their immortal souls.

Halvor, as well as his parents, thought that the house seemed very empty when the Reverend Mr. Evensen left them after having lived in their house for a year. He had married and moved into the new parsonage which had been built across from the church. It was, to be sure, not far away and they could visit each other often, but it was not the same as living under one roof. But on the other hand, it gave occasion for real festivity whenever the minister and his wife came over to spend the afternoon and evening. The minister's wife, or *Fruga,* as she was called, was pale and gentle and the most genteel woman Halvor had ever known. She was city bred, and there was something about her that made him regard her as one come from a different and more elegant world. And yet she was not particularly beautiful. Halvor was always happy when he was permitted to go to the parsonage with a pail of berries or some other delicacy as a present. Everything about the place was so tasteful. The house was not really as good or as large as his own home, but it was arranged so differently that to him it was the grandest place in the world. It was, in fact, so elegant that one unconsciously scraped the mud off one's feet before entering. In the living room was a contraption called an organ, which the boy had never seen before; and the minister's wife could sit down and play it so beautifully that Halvor was quite carried away from the world of reality.

Often he was allowed to sit up in the pastor's study and browse among the books. At home his whole library consisted of his schoolbooks, *Pilgrim's Progress* and Gjest Baardson's *Memoirs.* He liked both of these last named books, especially *Pilgrim's Progress,* which he considered a thrilling romance. He wondered at the strange names of the characters: Faithful, Evangelist, Worldly Wiseman, and all the rest. How did they all happen to have names that were unknown among people generally?

In the pastor's study he read *A Happy Boy* by Bjørnson, and enjoyed it; although it certainly was strange for anyone to sit down and write a book about a billy-goat and a tea roll. And that Marit from Heidegaardene! What a goose she was!

A Happy Boy was all right, but it was nothing in comparison with another novel which he ran across and which he read with such avidity that it made him breathless. It was the hair-raising story named *The Settlers on Long Arrow.* In it were accounts of bloody battles with Indians, murders, and many other fascinating things. This was interspersed with the most touching descriptions of the tender love between the hero, Keefe Dillon, and a beautiful Indian girl; it reminded Halvor most vividly of his own unrequited love for the school girl with the cute little nose and the curly hair; and he was moved to tears at the poor Indian maiden's declaration that heaven itself was not worth so much to her as a single hair from Keefe Dillon's head. It described his own feelings exactly. Such is love.

At about this time Halvor began to take instruction for confirmation, meeting with the rest of the catechumens at the parsonage each week. At these meetings he learned many things; one of the first was that it was just a lie that his father had found his baby sister under the root of an oak tree. This information he got from a younger brother of the minister. It was a shock. Not even his father was to be depended upon in everything that he said. From his books Halvor had learned much that he did not understand at all. He had long been able to rattle off what "Paul says to Titus --3:5—concerning baptism." For one thing he did not know the meaning of the word Titus. The figures 3:5 he of course was familiar with. They must signify either three dollars and five cents, or three feet five inches, or five minutes past three. Now he discovered that this was all wrong.

Trouble in the Congregation

There was trouble in the Springville congregation. Before the Reverend Mr. Evensen had been there two years there were some who were dissatisfied and wished to make a change. And, besides, they had now lived in America long enough to know that one was not absolutely obligated to have any minister at all unless one wished.

Everyone had to admit that Pastor Evensen was "an able man in the pulpit," and that if they could only live according to his preaching they would have nothing to fear. But he could not chant, and that was disappointing, to say the least. Furthermore, he had been heedless enough to offend a considerable number of his best parishioners by telling them that they drank too much. He had even, with the help of Søren Helgesen and Ole Kjeldalen, put through a resolution to the effect the no member of the congregation ought to put his foot inside of a saloon. There was, for example, young Hatleviken. He was the son of the parish clerk who was, as has been related, a great reader of Linderot's Book of Sermons, and one of the first settlers; and yet the minister had reprimanded him for sitting in Myran's saloon drinking and playing cards with John Tangen who, considering his limited opportunities, had more religious books in his house than anyone else in the community. To cap it all Evensen had mortally offended such a pious man as Klemmetsrud. On one occasion when Klemmetsrud was bemoaning the fact that there were so many

[65]

unconverted children of the world in the congregation, the minister had the effrontery to say that it was a good thing for him and the congregation that this was so, in view of the fact that it was these same children of the world who always were most generous when money was needed.

Klemmetsrud, poor man, had to hear many things that wounded him. One evening when he had called on two of the minister's best friends to see if they conducted family prayers in their homes, Søren had told him that the reason the streets of Jerusalem were so clean was that each man swept before his own door.

Klemmetsrud felt that something simply must be done. Such godlessness could be suffered no longer. That the pastor was not a real Christian he had long suspected, but until this time proof positive had been lacking. Now, however, he had made a discovery by the help of which he could determine with absolute certainty whether or not a man was a converted Christian. It was so simple that he marveled that he had not thought of it before. It had come to him as an inspiration as he sat in church one Sunday. The minister was reading from the portion of the Bible in which the apostles were given instructions as to how to go about their work:

"And into whatsoever house ye enter, first say, Peace be unto this house. And if the son of peace be there your peace shall rest upon it; if not it shall return to you again." (Luke 10:5,6). Klemmetsrud's eyes opened wide. Now it would be the simplest thing in the world to find out the exact state of Pastor Evensen's soul. One need only say, "Peace be to this house," and see what would happen. Klemmetsrud soon made a pretext to call at the parsonage, and the experiment worked beyond expectation. He shook hands with the minister and said, "Peace be upon this house." And he was overjoyed to notice plainly that the peace returned to him. Thank the Lord, there was no longer any doubt about it; the minister had not found the Lord! If further proof were needed he might also mention that Pastor Evensen had been unwilling to say that it was a sin for Hans Skogen to play the fiddle—an instrument in whose tones a true child could hear the Evil One himself.

Klemmetsrud could not help telling Søren Helgesen about his experiment and how the peace had returned to him. Søren only laughed at him. What must one think of a minister who associated with such a godless fellow—a man who had not come so far in Christian conviction as to be sure that dancing was a sin. He had said as much with great flippancy right to Klemmetsrud's face and he had even added:

"But I'll tell you what, Nils, to go about sowing suspicion of the minister and others, that's what I call sin. To sit and sleep in church and then sigh and find fault with the sermon you haven't heard, that is a sin; and to be as miserly as you are, that is a sin."

What more was needed to make it clear as day that both the minister and Søren were in the service of Satan? It was no more than a Christian duty to crush them both. He could not, of course, do it alone, but there were enough who would help him. It was strange how a case of this kind brought together both the over-pious and those who were notorious for their lack of piety. The extremes met.

The ill will toward the Reverend Mr. Evensen smoldered along well into the next year. Klemmetsrud and an old blasphemer with a poisonous tongue fanned the flame industriously. At last, when the minister was purported to have committed a worse piece of effrontery than usual, it burst into flames.

In the congregation there was an old man who was insane. To be sure he was counted sane enough, for his mania was of a kind that is very common and is not usually considered a symptom of insanity. He was a miser. He was old and had a great deal of money, much more than he could possibly spend before he died. He begrudged it to his family after he was gone. And still he worked and fretted to gain more, and deprived himself of necessities in order to hoard it up, knowing that he had no use for it and that he would soon have to leave it behind. What is this but a form of insanity?

Well, at this time the old man died. He had become rich by following literally his motto: "Thou shalt sell all that thou canst sell; and what thou canst not sell, thou shall feed to thy pigs; and what the pigs will not eat, thou shalt eat thyself."

This worthy gentleman had numerous relatives. They got up a great and splendid funeral for him, only to have Pastor Evensen shock the assembled multitude by announcing as his text: "It is easier for a camel to go through the eye of a needle than for a rich man to enter into the kingdom of God," and preaching a sermon on the sin of miserliness. No one dared look up, so painful was the situation. Everyone knew that the consequences would be dire. Martin Kaasa, the old man's son-in-law, was not a man to submit to such treatment. People even wondered if Søren Helgeson, as staunch a friend of the minister as he was, would defend him in this. For days this funeral sermon was the only topic of conversation. There were many who took a secret delight in it and thought it served the old skinflint right. Had he not refused to give a cent when they were trying to gather together a little money for Ole Findreng's widow and had he not been abusive besides? Søren declared outright that the minister had spoken nothing but the truth.

But the majority thought differently. It would not do to let the minister say anything he pleased and offend good people. He had better remember that it was the congregation which had hired him and which supported him. Klemmetsrud agreed with these people perfectly, maintaining that it behooved a clergyman to be meek and keep peace with everyone.

It was soon whispered around that Pastor Evensen ought to be removed. But to depose him for preaching against drunkenness or miserliness would not look good. Klemmetsrud knew that if a preacher were to be deprived of his office it must be on account of false doctrine; that seemed to be the most proper reason. But it was hard to catch Pastor Evensen in that. Klemmetsrud sat like a cat watching him during every sermon, after first having breathed a prayer for success in discovering something contrary to the Word of God in the discourse. But it was to no avail. The minister was so careful that Klemmetsrud grew almost desperate.

Luckily, however, the great controversy about slavery arose at this time. Pastor Clauson had just resigned from the Norwegian Synod because that body would not declare that under all circumstances it was a sin to be a slave or to keep slaves. Among the congregations everywhere there was great excitement. The ministers were compelled to take a stand. There was talk of hanging Professor Larsen because in an explanation demanded by *Emigranten* he had said that he had heard good reasons for the right of a state to secede from the Union. Klemmetsrud and his friends were much interested and pleased, for this was something to hold to. They read *Emigranten* and *Skandinaven* and were sure that everything Fleisher, Langeland, Johnson, and others wrote was the gospel truth. And there it was in black and white that the clergymen of the Norwegian Synod approved of and defended slavery, an institution which many of the members of the congregation had risked their lives to abolish.

Here they had proof in black and white that Pastor Evensen was as good as a slaveholder, for he did not conceal the fact that he shared the opinion that slavery "in and by itself" or "in its bare generality" could not be said of necessity and under all conditions to be a sin. There was no other way to keep a clear conscience than to give the minister his walking papers. Confound it! Those ministers in the Norwegian Synod were nothing but a flock of Rebels and slaveholders, which fact they had clearly shown when they expelled Rasmus Anderson from the school in Decorah just because he wanted to read *Skandinaven* without asking Professor Larsen's permission.

It was fortunate for Klemmetsrud's purpose that Pastor Evensen also in other respects taught what to Klemmetsrud and his followers were soul-destroying doctrines, even though it might be hard to prove them contrary to the Word of God. But soul-destroying they certainly were, as any true Christian could clearly sense. It could be proved that the minister had said that infants were not by nature pure and innocent, and that people ought not to go and hear a fly-by-night revivalist who had come to Springville to witness against dancing, cards, the Norwegian Synod, and other wickedness.

This man of God, who was obviously moved by the Holy Spirit, made Klemmetsrud very happy. He showed him a book by Luther which contained these words: "A dead mother cannot bring forth a living child." This could be interpreted in no other way than to mean that an unsaved or spiritually dead man like Pastor Evensen could not preach in such a way as really to convert anyone. It was therefore out of all reason to retain him any longer. The saying about the dead mother came in so very handy; it seemed actually providential that these words of Luther had come to his attention just now. He quoted them in season and out of season. He would not have forgotten them for anything in the world. With this little jawbone of an ass he would be able like Samson to slay his thousands.

Now was the time for action. He took a trip around, calling on the members of the congregation to sound them out and learn how many were in favor of ousting the minister. He went from house to house telling them what Luther had said. Then he sighed deeply and assured them that he had nothing against Pastor Evensen personally, but felt he must act according to the dictates of his conscience. He met with much encouragement. He found more people who agreed with him than he had dared hope. Old Kittel Strand promptly declared that he would "gladly help drive the Devil from the hill by the church." Kittel had no very good reputation, but it was gratifying just the same to find that he was willing to support a good cause. Hatlevik-Ole was also in favor of getting rid of the pastor, and he offered to see to it that his father, the clerk, took the same stand. As the old man lived with his son, the latter felt he had a right to control his vote. Ole, however, wished it to be clearly understood that his only reason for wanting the minister removed was that his teachings were contrary to the Word of God and the Catechism. It had absolutely no connection with the lecture Pastor Evensen had given him for drinking. Martin Kaasa thanked Klemmetsrud by a hearty handshake for having taken the initiative in this important matter and assured him that he would help him all he could. Tone, his wife, had declared she would never set her foot inside of the church so long as Pastor Evensen was the minister. Under these circumstances her husband could hardly go either. Both felt the need of going to communion so sorely that it was their Christian duty to get a new minister. They could not with a good conscience go as long as he was the one to administer the sacrament.

Hans Skogen did not know his own mind. He was secretly afraid that the new minister might order him to burn his fiddle. If he had only felt sure about that matter he would be inclined to make common cause with Klemmetsrud. Consequently he said only that he would think the matter over. And Klemmetsrud had to rest content with that.

So far all had gone better than Klemmetsrud had dared hope. He could only thank God that there was so much Christian principle in the congregation. He was very much elated, but had to admit that he had seen only those he had reason to believe would give him their support. He dreaded going to see some of the remaining members, but he had promised himself to pass no one by. And so he thought he might as well take the bull by the horns and call on Thrond Knudson and Søren Helgeson.

On his way to Thrond's he took a notion to drop in at the home of Ole Findreng's widow. She belonged to the congregation in a way, although she had no vote and was unable to contribute toward the support of the church. When Klemmetsrud disclosed the nature of his errand, the woman who was usually so meek and mild grew angry and scolded him roundly, calling him a hypocrite and a scoundrel, and showed him the door. She had never, she said, seen or heard anything but good of Pastor Evensen. Klemmetsrud could not understand what had gotten into the woman. She had apparently forgotten that she was only a pauper whose husband had committed suicide and whose neighbors had to help her. He bitterly regretted having given her a dollar. It was not right to do anything for a person whose heart was so wicked. So angry was he when he left that he threatened to bring her to the throne of grace in his prayers.

Arriving at Thrond's house he found him licking his spoon clean after having eaten his evening mush. "Is it you who are out so late?" asked Thrond.

"Yes, it's me , all right."

"Won't you sit up to the table and have some of our plain mush and milk?"

"Yes, thanks." He laid his chewing tobacco carefully on the window sill and sat down to the table. To start the conversational ball rolling Thrond remarked, "Well, it's a whopper of a moon we have tonight." Klemmetsrud agreed perfectly with that statement. Then after a short silence he began to explain his errand. It certainly gave him no pleasure, he said, to complain of the minister; but he felt it his duty to lay the matter of making a change before the people. Evensen had caused much offense by his treatment of some of the best people and oldest settlers. He took too much authority unto himself although he was, alas, no true Christian, a fact he had shown plainly enough in his attitude toward persons called to bear witness for the Lord. He had no ill will toward the minister personally, but one must obey God rather than men, and it was for that reason that he felt he must do his utmost to get Evensen out of the way.

Thrond had filled and lighted his pipe as he listened politely and in silence. It would never do to get into an argument on religion with Klemmetsrud, a man who preached such good sermons that one would think he had been educated for the ministry. But on the other hand Thrond thought it would be sad to lose Evensen. He was as learned as any preacher could be. He knew his relatives in Norway and they were good people, all of them. If one could not believe in Pastor Evensen, whom could one believe in? When Klemmetsrud claimed that his doctrine was all wrong, Thrond's head spun. A man who had studied so long surely must understand the Bible. It was crazy to think anything else. Thrond scratched his head and stammered something to the effect that perhaps the matter should be left to the government. He doubted that it was proper for uneducated laymen to talk about such things. He knew at least that it was the government that handled the case of the minister at home in Valders—it was Pastor Harbitz at that. The facts were these: There was a man who had twins christened and Pastor Hartitz charged a mark for christening them, as was right and proper. But, then, instead of charging eight shillings for churching the mother he charged sixteen shillings, just as if there had been two women to be churched instead of just one, since the babies were twins. Naturally the father felt he had been cheated and was sore at the minister. But—get him fired? Not at all. Pastor Harbitz was made to return the eight shillings, but that was all. He was allowed to keep his position. Thrond was not quite sure whether the same rule held in America as in Valders, but it probably did. At present he would make no promises. He wanted to talk to Søren first. Søren would surely know as much about such things as anybody in the church.

During this conversation Gunhild had come in. She needed no time to consider the matter but told Thrond he must not think of such a thing as being a party to any attempt to hurt the minister.

She believed him to be a true "Luthrian", and he was as handy about christening babies as any man could be. Klemmetsrud could not budge her.

By this time it was late. Too late, perhaps, to see Søren. But since he knew beforehand that the visit would be fruitless, he wished to get it over with as soon as possible.

Søren had just put up his horses after coming home from town, and was sitting smoking his pipe by the kitchen stove when there was a knock at the door. "Come in," he said. And in came Klemmetsrud with solemnly measured tread.

"Good evening, and thanks for the last time."

"Good evening; the same to you. Are you out so late?"

"Yes, so I am. And how are you?"

"Very well, thank you."

"Well, there is nothing better than to be well. If one has health one can always get along." He sat down. Søren waited in silence for what he knew was coming. At last Klemmetsrud managed to say:

"Well, I s'pose you know what I came here for?"

"Yes, I think I do. I take it you have come to pay me the money you borrowed last year to pay your church dues, and which you promised to pay in the fall."

"Why, Søren! You know I was hard up last year. I'll pay you this fall as soon as I have threshed. I should have paid you before, but . . ."

"Well, never mind about the money just now. I have heard what it is you are sneaking around for. I hope you don't think I'm going to have anything to do with that business."

"No. But I just wanted to ask you. I've got a right to that, haven't I?"

Søren replied that if Klemmetsrud had a right to ask he was also entitled to an answer. And he proceeded to give him an answer that caused his ears to burn and smart the whole way home. Never in all his life had he been treated so shamefully. But never mind; Søren would be in a pretty fix on the Judgment Day when he would have to give an account for every word he had spoken,

There was no use denying, however, that his reception at the last three places had been disheartening. Things looked dark. But the very next Sunday afternoon the sky cleared. He attended a prayer meeting at the Hatleviken home. It was conducted by the aforementioned lay preacher. And it was here that Klemmetsrud found sympathizers. Neither Thrond nor Søren were present, another clear proof that they were spiritually dead. Klemmetsrud was overjoyed to learn at this meeting that there was a rumor to the effect that Pastor Evensen had told an old man who was dying that he was too old to be saved. This came as manna to Klemmetsrud's soul. He wished to hear the details of the story, but unfortunately no one present seemed to know the particulars from first hand. But Martin Kaasa's wife, Tone, who claimed to have heard the story, was thoroughly questioned. She knew only, she said, that the minister had been called to the death bed of Anders Viken and that he had told the old man that since he was eighty years old it was no use wasting the Word of God on him; he was too old to be saved. Only the daughter of the deceased had been present. She had been taking care of her father and had opened the door when the minister came. He had asked her if she was alone with the sick man. Then he had gone in to her father's room, and there it was that he had expressed the impious words that had so shocked them all.

Klemmetsrud pricked up his ears. "So he asked Anders Viken's daughter if she was alone, did he? Why do you suppose he asked her that? One should, of course, put the best construction on all things, but that sure was a funny question. Think of it: A young minister enters a house to visit a dying man; and when a pretty girl opens the door he asks her right away if she is alone. It certainly looks suspicious." Klemmetsrud's voice had grown very low as he talked about so delicate a subject. And he went on to say that he felt it his duty to speak of it to a few of the brethren in all confidence and to ask what they thought of such conduct. By this time everyone was ready to admit that Pastor Evensen was a . . . well, enough said. One must not wrong him, but the truth was that he had spoken indecently to Anders Viken's daughter. Perhaps there was a reason for poor Mrs. Evensen's being so pale. At times she looked as if she had been crying. She, no doubt, knew better than anyone else what sort of man her husband was. It would be an act of charity to inform her family of what kind of a life he was leading so that they could take her home. She, of course, would not dare say anything against her husband; but her having grown so thin could be accounted for in only one way. Anyone who still wanted to keep Pastor Evensen was in Klemmetsrud's opinion absolutely without a conscience.

At the next prayer meeting all the usual crowd was present besides a great number of people who had never before attended these meetings. How closely a common cause had brought together these two elements—the sanctimonious members of the congregation and the irreligious who were members in name only. It was hard on the latter to have to sit with pious miens and listen to Klemmetsrud gloat over the horrors of hell fire. When the religious program was over, the complaints against the Reverend Mr. Evensen were taken up for discussion. Klemmetsrud began by explaining that he could not vouch for the truth of the dreadful stories that were being told about their minister, having always made it clear that he was only repeating what he had heard, and having always warned against putting the worst construction on things. What he based his complaint on was that he had taught false doctrines, caused dissension, given offense, and shown by his conduct that he was no Christian, and therefore he was unfit to guide others.

Upon hearing the story of what Pastor Evensen was supposed to have said to Anders Viken and his daughter, and how it was being interpreted, Søren went over to Thrond Knudson's to talk the matter over.

"Say, Thrond, I'll tell you what we'll do. I know you won't stand for any such slander any more than I. You're too good a man for that. Let's go up to the parsonage and offer to pay the expenses of a suit for slander. You are well-to-do and I know you'll back me in this."

As a matter of fact, Thrond was not at all sure of what stand to take but Gunhild said, "Yes, of course you'll go." And that settled it. And, besides, he felt rather grand and important to be taking such a leading part in congregational affairs. So off they started for the parsonage. Søren went to the point at once and asked the minister if he had heard the stories about him. As he had not, Søren told him what they were.

The pastor took the matter more coolly than they had expected. Thrond had felt sure the man would fly up in a towering rage and either excommunicate Klemmetsrud on the spot or have him arrested and put into prison, and he was very glad he was not among the slandermongers. To his utter amazement the minister only said, "Well, I hope neither of you believe that I said Anders Viken was too old to be saved or that I said anything out of the way to his daughter."

"No, of course, we don't believe it," said Søren. "Thrond and I only came to tell you that we will pay the costs of having Klemmetsrud punished for slander. We don't think it is right to let such things go. We thought perhaps it would be hard for you to pay for the suit, so we wanted to take care of that part of the proceeding."

Pastor Evensen, however, would not give his consent. But at last he agreed to call a meeting of the congregation and demand an investigation of the charges.

At this meeting the minister merely mentioned that he had heard that some ugly stories were being circulated about him and demanded to know who had started them. No one would admit having said anything. But Søren Helgeson would not see them let off so easy. He repeated what he had heard and stated that Klemmetsrud, for one, had gone around spewing the poison. He demanded, therefore, that that pious hypocrite should either apologize or be expelled from the congregation.

Then the storm broke loose! As it was impossible to withdraw, Klemmetsrud delivered himself of a lengthy discourse. He admitted that he had heard and repeated the story of Pastor Evensen's un-Christian utterances at Anders Viken's deathbed and of his ambiguous question to the daughter. All this, however, was of minor importance. The main thing to him was that Pastor Evensen was not Christian and that he defended false and pernicious doctrines. He closed by moving that Pastor Evensen be deposed, and he made the motion himself. As far as one could judge in a hurry, about one-third of those present voted for the motion; whereupon Klemmetsrud presented a petition signed by forty-eight men asking that their names be stricken from the membership of the congregation.

The pastor begged them to take more time to consider the step they were taking and also to state their reasons for withdrawing so that the matter could be discussed. But they would not listen. They wished to found a new congregation which should consist of only such as were true children of God. Søren Helgeson remarked that he for one was glad to be rid of Klemmetsrud and his ilk, and he moved that their names be stricken with thanks. This motion would undoubtedly have carried except for the fact that the Reverend Mr. Evensen objected to the passing of any such motion. It was, therefore, amended to read that the congregation regretfully consented to their withdrawal from the congregation. This motion was passed with one dissenting vote. Søren voted no. It was not with regret, he said, but with joy that he voted to let the slanderers out of the congregation. The minister gave him a severe reprimand for taking such an attitude. But afterwards they were as good friends as ever.

Thus it came about that there were two Lutheran congregations in Springville. Much dissension arose among the families. In some cases the husband wanted to belong to one and the wife to the other. In other cases parents and children were on opposite sides.

The Reverend Mr. Evensen called a big meeting in order that the whole matter might be thoroughly investigated. Each faction called in three or four pastors from the outside. At this meeting the complaints against the pastor were presented in writing. It was testified under oath that the Reverend Mr. Evensen had told the old man that he was too old to be saved. It was proved that he had refused to allow one of the first members of the congregation to partake of the sacrament of the altar and that in general he had been stubborn and self-willed so that it was evident that he had forgotten that he was not his own master but a servant who the congregation had hired for four hundred dollars a year plus festival offerings and fees for ministerial services, the amount which was to be determined by the means and inclination of the giver. Thus ended the investigation. The new congregation erected a church edifice beside the old one, in which place it stands today as a monument to the late sainted Klemmetsrud.

Off For Decorah

Halvor was now fourteen years old and had finished all his subjects in the country school. His father had not forgotten the conversation about sending his boy to Luther College. But it was hard for him to make up his mind to send him so far away—they were such good companions. He decided, however, that he would have to stand it. So one evening he went up to the parsonage and asked the pastor to write to Decorah to register the boy. In a few days a reply came saying that Halvor had been accepted, and the matter was settled. It was not until now that Søren mentioned the matter at home. He knew that Halvor was eager to go and that Anne would be glad to be rid of him. "Anne," he said, "please put Halvor's clothes in order and pack them. He is going to the school in Decorah." Anne was far from enthusiastic. She feared that they could not afford to spend so much on the boy. Furthermore, she was not sure but what it might be a sin for plain folks like them to aspire to such high things as to make a minister of him. It might be that no blessing would come of it and that it would be better to keep to their station. Nor could she see that Halvor was too good to stay at home on the farm and work like other boys.

Søren declared that the matter was settled; the boy was to be given a chance to study and Anne had to get busy and get his clothes ready whether she liked it or not. Halvor then went to town with his father. The clothes that were bought for him were much finer than any he ever had before. His mother sewed him a couple of bosom shirts. In order that he might not outgrow them too soon they were made so large that they nearly sawed his ears off.

On the Sunday before he was to leave he was confirmed all by himself. Of course everybody came to church that day to hear that boy of Søren Helgeson's who was so bright that he was going to study to be a minister. Poor Halvor was so proud of being the most important person in the church; it must be admitted he forgot what confirmation really meant.

After the services he had to go around and say goodbye to his friends, for he was to leave the same evening. Thrond and Gunhild went home with the Helgeson's for dinner. Thrond asked permission to give Halvor a five dollar bill, and Gunhild presented him with a pair of red striped mittens which she had knit for him but which he could never get himself to wear.

After much discussion with the minister it was agreed that Halvor would surely be able to find his way to Decorah alone even though he had never been on a train before. He was given careful directions about taking good care of his ticket and not giving it to anyone but the conductor, and not forgetting to change cars at Milton Junction. He was told to hold his chin up high and not be afraid of asking questions if he had any difficulties. The boy himself was confident that he could take care of himself, and the rest thought the same since he was a good talker and not a bit bashful.

Now he was actually ready to start. His dreams were about to be realized. In his pocket were fifty dollars. His trunk was packed and was already reposing in the wagon. There was no mistake about it; he was setting out to see the world.

Presently his father drove up to the door and called out that now Halvor must come if they were not to miss the train. At this the boy could hold in no longer. He struggled bravely to keep from crying, but when he said goodbye to his little sister the tears came in spite of his efforts to stop them. To their mutual surprise he and his mother made a discovery. They realized that they really were fond of each other even though the boy had always been told that he was in the way. It took them so long to say goodbye that at last Søren ran in to say that he could wait no longer. A lump rose in his throat when he saw how Anne took the boy's leaving, and he felt a new tenderness for her as he heard her call Halvor her own boy. They got to town so late that there was barely time for Halvor to get on board before the train rumbled away. Søren looked at it and had a strong desire to stop it and take the boy off again. But when it was out of sight he went in and bought a handsome piece of dress goods for Anne for having been so kind to Halvor. Then he drove home thinking how empty the house would be hereafter. But, of course, he had Anne and their little girl. He would make them as happy as possible. And in a year Halvor would come back for a visit.

Meanwhile Halvor was sitting by an open window in the coach staring out at the beautiful changing landscape. My gracious, what speed! What fun it was to be setting out on this wonderful adventure. If only his schoolmates, who had never been outside of Springville, could see him now. They would be sick with envy. He was a hero, going out into the wide world all alone, clad in a brand new suit and a white shirt, with a large sum of money in his pocket. He was going to study and learn so much that everyone would marvel at him.

As he whizzed along he wondered at there being so little difference between his home and the world, now that he must be at least a hundred miles away. A hundred miles! He could not refrain from smiling as he saw a house which was almost exactly like the house at home. It seemed to have the same number of windows—one, two, three, four—but before he could count any further the train had already roared over a little bridge and was slowing up at a station. And from the farm on the hill came the whining sound of a threshing machine. He could just barely discern the men working in the cloud of dust and chaff. And the man who was standing just outside of the cloud swinging a long lash over the backs of the horses looked so tall and straight that it might easily have been his father. He wondered what were they doing now at home. It was certainly hard to realize that only a few hours had passed since he was there. Then his thoughts turned to Decorah. What would the college look like? Everything would most likely seem serious and solemn there just as it did at home when his father and mother were going to communion. He decided to be obedient and diligent; then, surely, no harm would come to him. Thus he dreamed and dreamed until the train arrived at Milton Junction. Then the conductor reminded him that he must get off and wait a couple of hours for a train from Milwaukee which would take him farther on his journey.

Outside the station there was a flock of boys. They were laughing and talking all at the same time and seemed to be uncommonly happy. Halvor heard that it was Norwegian they were talking. He heard them mention Decorah and Professor Siewers. They also talked about "cramming," whatever that might be. He sidled up along the wall to get as close to them as possible and listened with open mouth. He gathered that the leaders were boys who had been in Decorah before and were going back there. It was a great relief to know that by following them he would be sure to land in Decorah. They certainly knew the way and they appeared to be intelligent fellows who had been out in the world before.

The fact that they used so many words and expressions that were new to him showed him that they were educated. He even learned to know the names of some of them. That thick-set fellow with the red hair they called Sjur Weeks; the light complexioned young man with a hooked nose and dancing eyes and a straw in his mouth was called Hogstul. Then there was Kjetil Børthe, and Joe Svelland, and Smith Thompson; and in the care of Børthe there was a little fellow, white haired and freckled like Halvor himself and wearing blue striped home made pants and a coat that was much too large. He, too, was on his way to the school for the first time, but he did not seem the least bit bashful. He laughed louder than all the rest. And Halvor heard the fellow they called Børthe tell someone that the little freckled youngster who was with him was named nothing less that Peder Olson.

Halvor wished very much to get acquainted with this jolly bunch but was too shy to talk to them. Soon, however, they noticed him standing there swallowing every word that they said, and one of them asked him if he was on his way to Decorah, which he, of course, told him he was. Then they all plied him with questions such as how old he was, what his name was, and where he was from, and so forth. Then one of them asked him if he knew the gender of the German diminutives "chen" and "lein." When he told them he did not understand what they were talking about they told him that if he did not know that, Professor Siewers would be very angry with him. But they laughed so heartily that Halvor knew it was a joke and laughed with them.

Just then the train came and Halvor boarded it with the rest of the boys and sat down in the same seat as the little fellow they had called Peder Olson. There they sat all day and far into the night enjoying the jokes and stories of their new friends. They were the finest, kindest, and jolliest boys Halvor had ever seen. And to think that he was to be one of their number!

Every so often the train stopped and other boys entered to be greeted by laughter and noise by the flock, and the fun increased with each addition to their number.

"Look, there comes Odven!"

"Well, if it isn't Christian Preus! And there is Mandt, and there Felland!" More greetings and more questions about everything and anything.

"But who are the boys with you, Christian?"

"Oh, they are Fosmark and Benny Bredeson."

"Is he a brother of Adolph, perhaps?"

"Yes, I should think you could see that."

"But who in the world is that kid?" asked the latest arrival, "that one over by the door with the blue striped pants who laughs so loud? He surely can't be going to college, can he?"

"Yes, he certainly is. He came with Børthe who says he is a dingbusted smart kid even if he is so small."

Thus the chatter continued until midnight when the town of Prairie du Chien was reached where they had to wait until morning to take the ferry across the Mississippi in order to board the train for Connover. Not one of the boys was extravagant enough to go to a hotel to sleep. They sat in the waiting room or went out for a walk, and they sang or talked until morning. Halvor thought the time passed much too fast. It would not have occurred to him to sleep and miss the fun. He struck up a friendship with Børthe's little protégé. They soon became great chums and each told the other the story of his life and all about his family tree. Halvor told Peder how strong his father was and how pretty his little sister was, and Peder gave an account of his family and relatives. They discovered that both had just finished the eighth grade. The friendship was formed and lasted as long as they lived.

In the morning the boys went up town in a body to see where they could get a frugal breakfast at the lowest possible price. Only a couple of them were flush enough to go to a hotel and eat a real breakfast. The rest bought a few slices of bread and a piece of sausage which they ate with great composure while waiting on the wharf for the ferry.

Over in McGregor a flock of new boys joined them, and there were new shouts of welcome and more noise and jokes until at noon they reached Connover. Here the boys who had been in Decorah before became very busy hiring livery rigs, bargaining with the drivers and arranging who was to go in each wagon. The railroad to Decorah had not been completed. They all pitched in as if their lives depended on getting to Decorah as soon as it was possible to do so. They dragged their trunks out of the baggage room and helped load them onto the wagons, and one load after another was soon on its way. Our friend Halvor was in a wagon with five others. Since each had a trunk and a satchel they were badly crowded, but that could not be helped because the fare was six dollars and there had to be six in order to make the fare a dollar apiece.

The drive from Connover to Decorah was the most enjoyable part of the trip. It was a beautiful sunshiny day, and the road along the valley was good. They sang and shouted, and the driver begged them to talk English so that he could enjoy the fun too. Halvor fell asleep and rolled off his trunk. He only knocked a finger out of joint and that added to the merriment. The road was downhill nearly the whole way and the miles seemed much too short. Soon they saw Decorah way down in the valley. Some of the boys stood on top of their trunks, craned their necks, and claimed that they could see the Luther College tower through the trees up on the bluff to the left. The road turned. There on the height toward the northwest stood Luther College, bidding them welcome! The horses trotted briskly over the bridge and up toward the stately building which fairly teemed with boys, big and little. The boys who were arriving stood up on their trunks, waved their hats and shouted, "Hurrah for Luther College!"

Decorah

Decorah! Strange that this name should have such a beautiful sound to our ears. It is merely the name of an Indian chief who decorated himself by painting a red stripe down his forehead and to the tip of his nose, and who beat his wife if she neglected to light his pipe or bring in the firewood. And yet how dear this name is to us. To our mind's eye it unrolls a picture in which the Creator has brought all the beauties of nature to a focus.

Splendid are the heavens. Fair is the earth. Beautiful are the narrow valleys with their overhanging cliffs and roaring waterfalls. Beautiful are the shores with the ocean beating against them. Beautiful are the prairies of the West where the eye finds no resting place but only great spaces everywhere, and one feels so small and insignificant that one says with the Psalmist, "Lord, what is man that thou art mindful of him."

Yes, the universe is wonderful. All is so well conceived and so perfectly made that one cannot imagine how it could be improved upon. And of all the beauty spots in nature, Decorah is a gem.

The Upper Iowa River winds its way between steep tree-clad hills, meanders through a low fruitful plain until it suddenly meets a perpendicular mountain wall and is compelled to turn off to the left. It flows along close beside this wall for a mile when it sees before it a still broader valley. It hesitates, and not knowing where it wishes to go, turns now to the left, now to the right and by sheer luck finds its way to where it again finds wooded hills on both sides and is spared the trouble of choosing its course.

In this lovely river valley lies Decorah. If one stands at the spot where the river leaves the cliff, one sees to the east the town with its freshly painted houses and its tall church spires, and to the northwest, a plain sloping evenly upward, ornamented by scattered houses and trees, which suddenly drops down almost perpendicularly to the river bed.

Upon the highest point and close to the edge of the cliff stands Luther College. The great stately main building faces a level plateau, the northern part of which is dotted with oak trees. Below it to the east, nestling in the valley, lies the city of Decorah.

Such is the picture that flashes upon the inward eye when we see or hear the name Decorah. It has become a very part of us, for not only is it the place where the happiest days of our youth were spent, but it is where our horizons were widened and where we learned that God is great in all His works and manifestations. The name also means much to our whole ethnic group, for Luther College in Decorah has been the center of its spiritual and cultural life.

It was not of such things, however, that Halvor Helgeson was thinking when as a young lad he first came to Decorah. We left him sitting on the top of his trunk looking all around as his fellow travelers were swinging their hats and shouting hurrah.

The wagon stopped in front of the main entrance, and the boys who had arrived earlier crowded around it. "Hello, Mandt! Hello, Christian! Have you had a good time this summer? How awfully tanned you are." And the fun which had been interrupted was resumed in attempts to run up the fifteen steps to the entrance door in three jumps.

Halvor and the other new boy whose acquaintance he had made on the trip helped each other lift their trunks down from the wagon and drag them into the hallway. Then, however, Halvor was in a quandary. What should he do next? The boys who knew the ropes were too busy to bother about the new ones. And Halvor sat down on his trunk and was very close to tears. His thoughts retraced the way down the shining railroad tracks straight back to Springville. It was too far to go home and ask his parents to let him stay there. Here he sat and did not know where to go next. In the rooms above him there was a deafening uproar. Everyone seemed to be having such fun that he did not dare ask anyone for advice. Even the youngster who he had come with had deserted his trunk and was standing in the center of a group of older boys laughing and joking quite as if he were one of the oldest boys of the school.

In the corner at the right of the entrance door he saw a door that was ajar, and in the room beyond, at a table, sat a man writing. He did not look like a college student. Perhaps it was Professor Larsen himself, and Halvor's knees shook at the thought. Just then the man looked up and saw the boy sitting there with a pleading look in his eyes. He rose and came out. It was surely Professor Larsen! He looked to be of middle age, was straight and strong and of medium height. His hair and beard were black, and he had a high forehead with a large scar running obliquely toward the right eye. Above the somewhat aquiline nose reposed a pair of spectacles behind which shone a pair of piercing eyes. He wore a black alpaca suit and a gleaming white shirt. His watch chain was worn around the neck and ended in his vest pocket. As he entered the hall he pulled out his watch and held it close to his eyes. Halvor sat wishing he were safe in Springville. But when the man spoke he knew at once that he had nothing to fear.

"Why are you sitting here?" asked the man. Halvor somehow managed to stammer that he did not know where to go. Professor Larsen asked him to come into the office.

"What is your name?"

"Halvor Helgeson."

Professor Larsen turned the leaves of a book in which many names were listed.

"Oh, yes, you are from Springville, from Pastor Evensen's charge, are you not?"

"Ya-as."

"Well, you are to study in Study Room No. 1 and sleep in Room No. 49."

But as Halvor stared as if he wondered what in the world was meant by "sleeping in No. 49," Professor Larsen took him out into the hall. Just then a young man came walking past.

"Oh, Molstad, will you be so kind as to look after this boy and show him where to set up his bed? He is to be in room No. 49."

And Molstad was a very kind fellow. He looked after Halvor with fatherly solicitude. He helped him set up his bed and fill his mattress with straw and carry his trunk upstairs and put his things in order. Then a bell ran, and Molstad said it meant that supper was ready. Accordingly, he took Halvor down into the big dining hall in the basement and kept him under his kindly protection. Here Halvor had a chance to see his new companions in a body. They seated themselves at the long tables, and then a tall young man tapped his plate for silence. The room suddenly became as still as a church while the young man said grace.

"Is that one of the teachers?"

"No, it is only Teisberg."

"What is Teisberg?"

"Oh, he is a *primaner*."[6]

"*Primaner*? What's that?"

"Why, don't you know what that is? A *primaner* is a student in the highest class."

"Oh . . ." Halvor stared at the *primaner*. He really did not look much different from the rest. But think of what fathomless wisdom he must have in that head of his. Halvor was informed that the other students sitting at the end of the table were also *primaners*. They ate and joked and were most jolly. "Well, who wouldn't be jolly," thought Halvor, "if he had got so high up in the world and knew so much."

There was more noise at the table than Halvor had expected. Several very attractive girls were walking around pouring tea and carrying in great piles of bread which disappeared with astonishing rapidity. And a nice elderly woman, Mrs. Crøger, went around supervising everything, and yet the boys laughed and rapped at the plates for attention and were not the least bit shy.

Halvor bravely ate his bread and butter and drank his tea, all the time thinking about how much better the food tasted at home. Presently the room grew quiet again as the same young man gave thanks. The minute he was through they all rushed up the stairs so that the whole building shook.

When Halvor had reached the hall above, he noticed two *primaners* engaged in conversation. Just then a girl passed by and disappeared into a room at the end of the hall. Halvor slowly sidled up to the two great men to hear a few words of the wisdom which surely must be falling from their lips. All he heard was this: "She is, *profecto*, getting to be a very good looking girl!"

So that was the kind of stuff they were talking about! What a shock! But, as far as the opinion they expressed was concerned, Halvor agreed perfectly with them. By using his ears he soon discovered that most of the student body shared this admiration for "the young ladies" of whom they got occasional glimpses. He did not fall in love with any one of them for the time being. He did not dare to do so.

He spent the evening walking around and after a while he began to wonder what could be the matter. He felt such a strange weight resting on his chest. Finally it came to him that it was longing for his father and little sister and for the year-old colt and his friends at home in Springville that bothered him. Just then, however, the bell rang again and the boys stormed down into the dining hall and he with them. First they sang a hymn, then they sat quietly and reverently while Professor Larsen read a chapter from the Bible and offered an evening prayer.

Then the younger boys had to go to bed at once. But where was No. 49? With trembling voice Halvor ventured to inquire of an older boy, and got this reply, "Oh, go to Texas!" Almost immediately, however, the impatient young man regretted what he had said and added. "Well, come along and I'll show you. Now, be careful not to oversleep tomorrow or it will go with you as it did with Johan Huss."

Halvor did not dare ask how it went with Johan Huss, and, besides, he was too sleepy to care. He hurried to bed and knew no more until he was awakened by a man walking through the room ringing a bell so large that he could hardly swing it. It was already broad daylight and Halvor jumped up and into his clothes and hurried downstairs. Fortunately he met his friend Peder Olsen and with him he had no reason for feeling shy. That kid already felt as much at home as if he had been born in the place. He had plied everybody with questions about everything and had found out that the first thing they were supposed to do in the morning was to wash. He had already bought a wash basin which he offered to share with Halvor, and the two boys went to the wash room together.

Well, now that was done, and Halvor was ready to go to the breakfast table and morning prayers. For the present, at least, he was safe from the terrible punishment meted out to those who overslept. An hour after the morning devotion everyone gathered in the large chapel in the north end of the third floor. The president of the college now made a speech to the boys concerning their duties, and Halvor realized at once that he would have to be very careful in his behavior and study hard if he were to be permitted to remain at the school. He decided to do his best and felt sure that then he would be able to get along all right.

He sat down in the back row from where he could view the long rows of boys, all of whom looked as if they knew more than he did.

Up there in the front sat the grown-ups whom he had heard called *primaners* and who presumably knew all the languages there were. And in a row along the wall behind the desk at which the president was standing sat the other five teachers. Halvor grew dizzy at the thought of how much they must know to be able to teach even *primaners*. They all seemed to be of an age—about the same age as his father. But, of course, they must be very old to have had time to learn so much. Now the roll of the upper classes was called; then that of the new students whose applications had been received. Halvor had barely the courage to say "Present" when the name Halvor Helgeson was called, and when that was over he felt a little bit taller than before. He was actually numbered among the students of the college. At the parsonage at home he had seen a directory of the students at Luther College, and he reflected that the next time such a list was published his name would be included. He could imagine with what joy his father would scan the list until he found his boy's name.

His gaze fell upon another new boy. He was so very thin that Halvor decided he would have no trouble in licking him if he ever had to do so. In spite of his extreme thinness he seemed very much alive. He had an extremely long nose. His eyes fairly sparkled with animation. Next to his nose these were his most noticeable features. It seemed to Halvor he could see that this boy's name was Aasmund—but no, his eyes had deceived him for when the president called the name Magnus Hermanson the boy answered "Present" so loudly that everyone turned to look at him.

So his name was Hermanson! He was the oddest looking boy Halvor had ever seen, and he decided to get acquainted with him as soon as possible.

When the ceremony of roll call was over, the schedule of classes was given out and for the rest of the day they had nothing to do but study this schedule in readiness for the next day when classes would begin. Halvor got his copy for *Sexta* as his class was called and

[93]

went down to a ledge of the cliff behind the college and began to commit it to memory in dead earnest. He had never realized how many hours there were in a week. And there seemed to be so many classes that he could not understand how the boys could find time to sleep and play ball and fish or do any of the things he had heard them talk about. It was only on Saturday afternoons and on Sundays that there were no classes, and on Sunday they had to go to church, he had been told.

The scenery around him was too beautiful, however, for him to learn his schedule. Directly below him on the plain he could see a big crowd of boys getting ready to play baseball. Farther down by the river there were some boys who were undressing to go swimming. Halvor was about to clamber down when the boy named Hermanson came and sat down beside him. They looked at each other in silence for a while.

"What are you so happy about?" asked Halvor.

"What I'm so happy about? Why, do I look so happy?"

"Yes, you surely do."

"Well, why shouldn't I be happy? Here I am in college where I have a chance to learn so much. You're happy too, aren't you? Where are you from? What is your name? Is your father rich?" These and many more questions were asked.

Halvor gave an account of himself. He told his name and that he was from Springville and that his father was an uncommonly fine man and that he had a little sister that was the prettiest little girl he had ever seen. And Hermanson, who had already learned that it was not proper to call college boys by their given names, called Halvor just Helgeson to his great surprise, and told him everything about himself. They soon became so intimate that Hermanson confided to Halvor that he intended to go through college in two or three years, so hard did he intend to study. He could not afford to go very many years anyway, and he had decided to become a minister as soon as it was possible, having heard that there were many places where ministers were needed but could not be had because there was such a scarcity of them.

"I suppose you intend to be a minister, too, Helgeson?"

"Yes, of course, why else would my father send me here?"

Thus the boys talked on until it was all settled that they were going to try to become ministers in neighboring parishes so as to be able to help each other in their work, and so that they would be able frequently to take their respective wives and children and pay each other visits. Then they strolled around in field and forest until the day was done.

The following day the real work was to start.

Halvor was scared when at nine o'clock the next morning he reported in the big classroom where the first class was to be in Norwegian. There sat his friend Peder Olson with Jensen's *Laese-bog* and *Modersmaalets Grammatik* before him, waiting eagerly for a chance to show how smart he was. He would be only too glad to recite for all the rest. Then the teacher came. He was a tall man with a bushy beard and small bright eyes. His vest was unbuttoned and his trousers hung so low on his hips that one might expect them to drop down at any minute. He sat down at his desk, scratched his head and rubbed his eyes. Then he said:

"One speaks in sentences."

This was the first thing Halvor learned at Luther College, and it stuck by him. Later he learned many things which lay in hopeless disorder in his brain like so much driftwood. But one truth always stood out in bold relief, namely: "One speaks in sentences."

He had classes in English, arithmetic, German, Latin and other subjects. It was enough to make one crazy the first few days. But little by little things began to shape themselves together so that Halvor was able to get his feet on the ground. He discovered that one must not take things too seriously. He soon got so that he could repeat such Latin phrases as *mensa rotunda* and *stella remota* without trembling.

But Latin certainly was tiresome stuff. All the boys agreed in that. There was not a bit of fun in it until one got so far in the vocabulary as *rostrum*, meaning trunk of an elephant. Then Latin suddenly became interesting to everyone except Hermanson. From that day on he was continually twitted about his nose by the boys who continually asked him if he knew what the Latin word *rostrum* meant. At last he was called nothing but "Rostrum," which name he bore throughout his college course.

His first year at college always seemed to Halvor a beautiful but indistinct dream. The time went so tremendously fast. The scenery was so beautiful; the new friends were so jolly and kind. It was such fun to play baseball and to go swimming and to wrestle, and it was such an everlasting struggle to learn the lessons. One simply had no time to count the days or weeks.

The events of the first year that stood out most clearly later in life were the first holiday, the Christmas tree in the college dining room, the first examinations, and the appearance of the first issue of the college paper. It was during the fall of Halvor's first year at college that this college paper was started. It was called *Svein Uraed* and was written by hand. Halvor was intensely interested in this publication and saved the first issue for many years. There was not much to it. It contained only some announcements that were supposed to be humorous and a long poem entitled "An Unsuccessful Courtship by Mail." In Halvor's opinion, at the time, it was the greatest of all literary masterpieces. Below are a few excerpts of it. It was considerably longer but we must say as did Wessel in "The Fork":

An irreparable loss it is, alas,
To the reader, myself and the world en masse
That in memory only this fragment is left.
Of the best parts, I trow, we are bereft.

The excerpts are as follows:

> *'Twas on a day in June*
> *When nature was in tune*
> *In the vale of Mississippi*
> *That our Henrik grew quite dippy.*
> *Cupid's cruel dart*
> *Did pierce his manly heart*
> *And gave to him the notion*
> *To be right quick in motion*
> *And write a billet doux*
> *To a maiden whom he knew.*
> *"Why not?" you say.*
> *Be silent pray,*
> *And let me tell*
> *My story well.*
> *The fact was this:*
> *The friend was feminini generis.*
> *At Christmas tide*
> *He saw her glide*
> *So neat and nice*
> *Across the ice*
> *At that first glance*
> *He fell in trance.*
> *You may believe*
> *That up his sleeve*
> *Sir Cupid laughed*
> *To think his shaft*
> *Had hit its mark.*
> *And Henrik's heart*
> *Did sting and smart*
> *His head did whirl,*
> *He wrote to the girl.*

Then the poem relates in great detail how the letter was mailed and how it reached the girl.

She broke the seal
And gave a squeal
Turned white as meal
Then rosy red
As jam on bread;
For the letter said:
Beloved Miss,
My source of bliss,
I now must tell
That I am well.
If I might know
You, too, are so
I should be glad
And never sad.
I have today
Something to say,
To which give heed.
It may indeed,
Bring happiness.
Can you not guess?
I love you dearly
And most sincerely.
If in your breast
You find the least
Affection tender
Your heart surrender.
Be mine, I pray;
And name the day."

By the title of the poem one may know that the courtship was not successful.

The first holiday at Luther College none of the boys will ever forget, no matter how many other things they may have to remember.

A couple of weeks after the opening of the school, the boys began to talk that it was time to take a holiday. It was an unwritten law that they were entitled to one holiday in each month. There was to be one now. It was not so much that they needed a rest but because it was time to gather nuts and grapes and other good things for Christmas.

A crowd of boys had gathered outside along the wall one evening after supper. They were of the unanimous opinion that someone must go and remind Professor Larsen that it was time for a holiday. The weather promised to be fine, so the holiday ought to be set for the next day. Two of the most foolhardy upper classmen were, therefore, appointed to negotiate with the president. The crowd waited with bated breath for the messengers to return and announce the result. Halvor was as anxious as anyone. How he admired the boys who actually had the courage to go to Professor Larsen on such an errand. He was worried on their account. But there they came, alive at least! He gave a sigh of relief. It could be seen from afar that their mission had been successful, for they were tossing up their hats as they came tearing down the steps in such breathless haste that they could barely gasp: "He said yes!"

There was, of course, great rejoicing. But they were promptly told that they must go to the study rooms and study their lessons as usual. That is, they must at least pretend to study. For if anything is impossible it is for a carefree college boy to study in the evening when he knows the next day is to be a holiday and the weather promises to be fine. That is beyond human power.

The next day the sun rose brighter than ever before and not a cloud was to be seen. The boys were up early; and when at morning devotion the hymn, "Now thank we all our God," was announced, they joined in with all their hearts and lungs for they really felt thankful to God because it was so good to be alive.

Halvor Helgeson, Hermanson, Monson, Lars Ueland and a few others of the younger element decided to go to the woods. But first they must have a swim. Down the steep cliff behind the college they clambered in big jumps, then they raced across the plain, then off went their clothes in a tearing hurry, then head first they dived into the river. It really was pretty cold, but shucks, one could easily get warmed up again.

After the swim a dispute arose as to what to do next. Hermanson wanted to fish, but no one else was of the same mind although no one would have objected to having fresh fish for supper. Monson had ten cents which he was willing to spend for the common good, so nothing would do but to go to town and buy cookies which they knew would be a blessing before the day was over. This done, it was decided that the first trip should be to Ice Cave which they had heard so much about.

Half a mile north of the city there towers a high cliff. Inside of it there is a cave extending about halfway up to its top. In this cave there is always ice to be found, whence comes its name. The boys found the cave and went in. They did not get far, however, before it got as dark as pitch, and they had to feel their way back. In doing this they chanced to find some candles left by former explorers. They lighted them and by their light were able to crawl way to the end of the cave. What made the trip more thrilling was that at times they had to crawl on their stomachs, so low were certain parts. What if the wall should cave in and bury them? On all sides were rocks that had evidently loosened and fallen down. It was perhaps best to get out again. How warm the sun shone outside. No wonder that God saw the light and that it was good.

Above the opening to the cave the cliff is so steep and bare that it is a difficult feat to climb to the top. Monson was set on trying it, so the rest must do the same. A chance to get killed was always worth trying. They succeeded in climbing it without a mishap and looked around them. Far below them lay the city, and close beside a bluff which could be seen toward the west was a flour mill driven by water springing out of the cliff and conducted to the mill through a long pipe. Yonder on the height toward the west lay their dear home, Luther College, towering proudly against the skyline. Great Scott, what a joyous thing it was to be alive! From their high position the boys could even see Professors Siewers and Landmark strolling leisurely in the direction of the town, and they wondered if these gentlemen talked Latin when walking all by themselves.

But this was not gathering nuts and grapes! That was the purpose of this holiday. But what of it? The few cookies which Monson had bought were hardly sufficient nourishment, and having nothing else to eat they had to go back to the college for dinner. After dinner the younger boys thought it was their turn to play baseball. Monson was indispensable, being a master baseball player. Small as he was he could strike the ball so that the sound of the impact was like a gunshot. And when he ran one would think that he had been shot out of a cannon. No matter where he happened to be when someone else batted the ball, he could make a dash and grab it before anyone else could even see which direction it had taken. Since the ball game seemed all important just now it was decided to let the nutting go until the following Saturday half-holiday when they would make up for lost time. Peder Olson was bound to pitch, insisting that he was a master at it. But Hermanson batted the ball straight into his face and he fell down as if dead. In a moment, however, he opened his eyes and immediately started to berate Hermanson for being so clumsy that he could not bat a ball into the air. When they were tired of playing baseball they began to amuse themselves by running races and wrestling.

Since so many of the boys were gathered in one spot Halvor had a chance to admire the heroes of the college about whom he had heard such remarkable stories. There was Bentson who could jump twenty-one feet in a running broad jump and ten feet jumping backward. He was thin and scrawny and did not appear to be as proud of his exploits as he certainly had a right to be. They begged him to give an exhibition, but he was heartless and refused. And there was no one who cared to try to break his record.   Sagen offered to wrestle with Hogstul or Nordby or anyone else who cared to take him on.   He threw Hogstul to the ground and skinned his nose in so doing.   This feature was just beginning to heal since its last skinning.   But Hogstul did not mind in the least.   This spirit was characteristic of the Luther College boys.   They only laughed at hurts.   They scrapped and got over it.   They were so jolly as almost to seem flippant.   It was not their style to talk about religion, but everyone who attended the school for a while seemed to imbibe a deep respect for everything honorable and true.   And they were closer to heaven than they are today with their consciences scarred in the hard struggle for existence.

When the holiday was over the boys ached in every limb.   So tired was Halvor that he thought of his bed up in No. 49 as his dearest friend.   But it would not do to go to bed until nine o'clock at the earliest.   Would that he were old enough to smoke and then he might go to the smoking room from whence issued noise and merriment which could be heard a long ways off.   He could not resist going to the door and looking in.   There he saw a great number of happy boys who were over eighteen and were therefore permitted to smoke.   Through the thick cloud of smoke which filled the air could be discerned the faint outlines of Thoen and Hans Johnson who were standing on one of the tables giving a concert.   Thoen was singing tenor with an occasional shrill discord, while Johnson with his very deep voice sang the bass of "Lift Up Your Eyes, Desponding Freeman."   An appreciative audience laughed and applauded and begged for another stanza.

It was hard to get back to work the next day, but there was no escaping it.   A couple of boys were so bold, however, as to protest, insisting that there ought to be one day more since those who had picked grapes and nuts had really been working and had had no real holiday.   They felt they were entitled to a day of rest.   Their only consolation was that Saturday was coming soon and with no classes in the afternoon they might then get a little relaxation.

During all this time Halvor had all but forgotten his father, mother, and sister. It was high time for him to write them a letter. He wrote and told them everything—all about his friends, and that he had been praised for his good work in Latin and that his money was all gone and would Father be so kind as to send him a few dollars. His father, who realized that as Halvor progressed in his education he would naturally need many expensive books, sent the money gladly.

Halvor and his friend Hermanson owned a lamp in partnership and sat together evenings studying and helping each other with their lessons. It was really only fun after they had gone through the first difficulties and knew what was required of them. But it took hard work. The prospect of another great holiday cheered them on, for the fourteenth of October was not far away. There was always a big celebration on that day as it was the anniversary of the dedication of the college. The day was spent like any other holiday except that in the evening there was a program in the dining hall. Several of the teachers and one *primaner* made speeches. Ellestad, Nordby and Førde had practiced some songs which they presented. Halvor had never imagined that singing could be so beautiful. It was quite different, indeed, from hearing old Hatleviken leading the singing in the church at Springville. When the speeches and music were over, the whole building was illuminated. A light had been set in every window. These were now lighted. From the outside it looked as if the whole building was on fire way up to the highest window in the tower.

If one walked a little ways off toward Professor Siewer's house it looked as if a new constellation had appeared in the sky with numberless clear stars in regular arch and row formation. And the boys thrilled with admiration and shouted hurrah, feeling that they would gladly die for Luther College if they could serve her thereby.

Winter was coming on. The cold north wind blew across the college campus, sweeping the oak leaves into great heaps. And the boys went down to the river every day to see if the ice was thick enough for skating. They did not have patience to wait. It was too cold to play ball, and they had been strictly forbidden to go swimming; otherwise they would surely have done so. At last, one day there was a thin sheet of ice covering the river, and Peder Olson could contain himself no longer, but simply had to try it to see if it would hold him since he was the smallest of all the boys. No, thanks! Crack went the ice, and splash went the water, and down went Peder. But soon he stuck his head up through the hole in the ice and called for help. Then, of course, the rest all went to his rescue. Professor Larsen could not reprimand them for doing the duty and saving a comrade. So they fairly raced to see who could plunge into the water first. And what a glorious cold bath they had! Perhaps they might be lucky enough to catch a cold and get excused from classes the next day. Having finally got Peder Olson ashore, they could not think of letting him walk up the hill, and he was glad to let himself be carried up to his bed. Then everyone had to change clothes while they talked over the heroic deed they had just performed. What sport it was!

Professor Larsen, however, was not so touched by the occurrence as they had expected. He knew only too well it was not zeal for saving a human life that had motivated them since everyone knew that the water was only three feet deep. But the boys were much chagrined to think Professor Larsen was unable to appreciate a heroic deed when he saw one.

In a few days the ice became so strong that it was impossible for anyone to fall through. The boys who had money bought skates, and the others tried to borrow a pair as often as possible. Ole Arntson was now the hero of the day, being the best skater. This was a much greater honor than having the highest marks.

Merry Christmas

Hermanson and Helgeson sat opposite each other at their table in the study room working hard to learn the Latin vocabulary for the next day. Hermanson was always diligent because he was trying to finish his course in half time. But Helgeson was in no such hurry. If he could only finish one year at a time he would be content. Just now, however, he was studying most industriously. He dared not do otherwise for it was about time for Professor Larsen to make his tour of inspection of the study rooms as he used to do each evening. He had a very bad habit, namely, that instead of stalking along so as to give the boys a chance to become engrossed in their studies, he walked so very quietly that no one knew before he was right in the room. He did not even slam the door as most people do. If two boys should happen to test the strength of their index fingers and someone else had to step over to hold the lamp so that it should not tip, one could be sure that when they looked up they would find Professor Larsen right there. The door would not have been opened and no one would know when or how he had entered. It was most uncanny.

On this particular evening Halvor sat quietly studying, waiting for Professor Larsen to make his round so that he might dare to bring out from its place of concealment behind his text books the novel *Jack Harkaway.* He had bought this book down at Buck and Rabers, and it was so thrilling that it kept him awake nights. At last Professor Larsen came, looked around the room and left, having ascertained that all were working hard. Then even Hermanson, contrary to his custom, laid his book aside, bent over the table and whispered, "Say, Helgeson, do you know that it is only a little more than a week until Christmas?"

Helgeson had thought about it considerably. In fact the boys had talked about it early and late, for at Christmas there was a two weeks' vacation. Great guns, how fine that would be! Those who were fortunate enough to live near Decorah were, of course, going home, and they were kind enough to invite one or more of their friends to go home with them. Hermanson was going to visit relatives in the country and he invited Helgeson to go with him. Helgeson, however, could not decide whether to accept the invitation or not, as he was nourishing the slender hope that perhaps his father might still take a notion to send him money to come home for Christmas. Every afternoon when mail was distributed he stood with palpitating heart waiting for his name to be called. And one day his turn came. He held in his hand a letter addressed in his father's handwriting. But, alas, it said that although his father and mother would like very much to have their son come home for Christmas, the trip was too long and too expensive, so he would have to try to have as good a time as possible in Decorah. And in order to help him make it a Merry Christmas his father sent a five dollar bill. From his mother he might expect a box containing Christmas cakes, a whey cheese, and some new shirts. With this he would have to try to console himself. He decided to go with Hermanson.

On the last day before the vacation no one knew his lesson, all having more important things to think about. The younger boys hated their Lokke and Madvig and their Cornelius Nepos quite as bitterly as the older boys hated Cicero, Livy, and Homer. Having classes the last day was enough to make one desperate. But such was the absolutely unreasonable and ridiculous rule of the college, and one had to make the best of it and crawl through the classes in one way or another. How could anyone study with his head full of thoughts about cream mush, spare ribs, and Christmas carols, and who would give a hang about who was the father of Alcibiades or any other of the miserable Greeks that Cornelius Nepos was always preaching about.

Time dragged, but at last evening came and the textbooks were flung aside with contempt. Now they might lie there undisturbed while their owners were gathering strength to do battle with them again.

A few of the boys who lived very near Decorah could not wait but left the same evening. Hermanson, Helgeson, and some others were to set out on their journey the next morning. Their driver had arrived and it remained only to get an early start in the morning.

The weather the next morning was so very cold that Halvor froze his face before he got down town, so he decided to stay in Decorah—the severity of the weather was his only reason for so deciding.

He had, to be sure, heard other boys tell that they had a very good time at the college during the holidays. It was told that the boys who remained had parties in the dining hall to which the daughters of the professors and their friends came, and that they played "numbers" and other games, so that one got acquainted with the girls. This, however, had nothing to do with his decision; so he said, at least.

Accordingly he walked back to the college and roamed around the building and was bored to death. Incredible as it may seem, he took one of the despised textbooks and studied it, just to pass the time away, for he could not possibly spend the whole day writing one letter home. At the supper table it seemed desolate because less than half the boys were present. The next day was Christmas Eve. Things began to take on a holiday air. They were allowed to sleep an hour later than usual, and upon arriving in the dining hall they discovered there had been a great change for the better in the menu. Instead of the usual coffee, bread and butter, there was now

Christmas raisin bread, sausage, and cheese; and the coffee had quite a different taste from what it usually had, for they were allowed to pour milk into it themselves and to help themselves to loaf sugar. One might almost imagine one were attending a party at home.

In the evening there was to be a gathering in the dining hall. The boys dressed up in their very best and were all anticipation. They had heard that some kindly disposed people had provided a small gift for each student. It could not be very much because the donors were not very well-to-do.

An hour after supper they gathered in the dining hall. It was quite proper to laugh and joke, and the older boys who had been to such affairs before were not afraid of looking even a professor's daughter in the eye and talking to her. But for Halvor that was out of the question. His shyness caused him misery. He felt also that his clothes did not fit very well and that his boots were clumsy. Matters did not improve when the presents were given out. When Halvor's turn came he received a comb and a mirror. He did not dare but say thanks, but in his heart he was sure that the present was intended as a hint to him to keep his stiff mop of hair in better order and to look in the glass and see how freckled he was. But how could he help that? His hair simply would not lie flat and freckles could not be scrubbed off. At home in Springville no one made fun of him on account of his looks. He was as good as anyone there.

Then Professor Larsen gave a talk on the message of Christmas. It was so cordial and cheerful and simple that Halvor forgot everything else and his heart filled with joy as he thought of the child that was born in Bethlehem.

Christmas day passed much like other holy days. There were services in the chapel and a spirit of peace and joy pervaded the place during the rest of the day. There was one difference, however, for in the middle of the afternoon they were invited to the dining hall for afternoon coffee.

Halvor was just beginning to find the vacation tiresome and wish he had gone with Hermanson when he heard that on December 27th, or "Third Day Christmas" as it was called, there was to be a party in the dining hall that promised to be enjoyable.

It was Mrs. Brandt who sponsored these gatherings. She was always contriving ways to give the college boys pleasure of one kind or another. The parsonage was on the campus and the boys all regarded it as a second home. Each Sunday Mrs. Brandt invited some of them to spend the afternoon, and all of them looked forward with pride to the time when their turn would come to receive such an invitation. And when they got it and went over to the parsonage, they always found Mrs. Brandt to be the very soul of friendliness. She shared the sorrows of the younger boys; she mended their clothes and taught them manners. In her heart there was room not only for her own family but for the whole congregation and for the two hundred students of the college.

At the Christmas parties in the dining hall she was indispensable. If she was not there, the games would fall flat. She knew any number of amusing and harmless games, and she managed things so that none of the shy young boys were neglected. She enjoyed it all like one of them.

Our friend Halvor was not sure whether he dared go or not. But he decided to look on at least. He found himself as inconspicuous a place as possible in a corner and sat looking at the "young ladies" and a number of other girls who were sitting at the other side of the room; all the time he was wondering if it would not be best to take flight.

But now they were beginning to play "numbers," and before he knew it he had joined in the game. Mrs. Brandt took charge of him and gave him courage. The fun of the game consists merely in chancing to sit beside a girl who one likes.

Halvor sat fearing and hoping that someone would call number twenty-two, so that he would have to walk way across the hall in plain sight of everyone and sit down between two of the dangerous girls. He liked them, but he was afraid of them. At last his turn came. His number was called—and, well, if it wasn't one of the professor's daughters! It was the very one he had most admired at a distance and on whose account he had decided not to go to the country. In a trance he walked in the direction from whence the voice came and, strangely enough, he managed to find his way. He nearly sat down in her lap, however. It was only a friendly push from a fellow student in the next chair that prevented this catastrophe. Now the goal was reached! But what was the use? He could not think of a word to say. His cheeks burned, his hair stood on end, and he could not even manage to hide his shoes under the chair.

Fate was kind, however, for it was not long before his number was called by a girl with whom he did not feel shy. She was one of the college maids through whose kindness he had often received a sandwich down in the kitchen when he was hungry between meals. By reason of her great size she went by the name of "Great Eastern" among the boys. She was one of the most popular of all the persons connected with the college. Halvor could sit beside her at his ease. And yet—strangely enough—if he had only had the courage to talk to the pretty young girls he would gladly have given a tooth.

Thus the vacation passed and Halvor began to look forward to the return of the boys and the re-opening of school.

When Hermanson returned Halvor told him he had had an "awfully" good time, but he was not sure whether he was lying or not. Hermanson said he had had a wonderful time and had fared sumptuously every day. He knuckled down to his studies with his usual zeal at once and he pulled Halvor along with him. The mid-year examinations were at hand. The thought of them hung over the boys like a nightmare. There was now to be an investigation to determine how much or how little they had retained of what had been taught them. Halvor discovered to his horror that he had forgotten everything. He hunted around in his cranium desperately, but all he could find there were a few Latin phrases and a few scraps of Norwegian grammar.

Thus Passes Both
Winter and Spring

"How do you think you will fare in the examinations?" asked Hermanson.

"Oh, it can't help but go badly," said Halvor, "for now all I know is the 'One speaks in sentences' and that an elephant's trunk is called 'rostrum' in Latin."

But when the time came he got along incredibly well. He came through the ordeal with honors, in fact, and was as proud as if he had taken the final examination in theology and had received the highest mark.

Not long after the examinations Halvor fell into disfavor with the teacher in German. There was a little rascal in the class, a boy who never knew his lessons. He and Halvor were good friends and sat at the same desk. Halvor never could resist the temptation to help him out by whispering the answers to him when he was stuck. The class quite frequently began by the teacher's saying to this boy: "Now, Erickson, you may tell me all you know." And when Erickson remained silent, "Sit down Erickson. It appears you know nothing." Or the teacher might say: "Erickson, tell me the gender of the German diminutives 'chen' and 'lein'."

"Masculine."

"Nonsense! Bredesen?"

"Feminine!"

"Bosh! Helgeson?"

"Neuter."

"Right, my friend. That is the way the rest ought to learn their lessons, too."

Then one day the teacher began: "Erickson, give me the ten masculine nouns ending in 'e' that belong to the mixed declension."

"Buchstabe, Friede, Funke, Gedanke, Name, Same, Schade, Wille, Glaube, Harpe," answered Erickson without the slightest hesitation.

The teacher was speechless with astonishment. "So you really knew that, Erickson? Or am I only dreaming? Let me see that you turn over a new leaf now, Erickson so we. . . . What is it you are whispering to Helgeson, Erickson?"

No reply.

"Well, Helgeson, what was it that Erickson whispered to you?"

Halvor did not want to answer, but Erickson nudged him and said, "Go ahead. Tell him."

"He said, 'That fool thinks I know my lesson. But I read the answer out of the book.'" At that Halvor burst out laughing and the teacher grew angry.

"Erickson, you may come up here. And you, Helgeson, may leave the room—because you laughed," he added.

Halvor left the room. But he was very curious to see what punishment would be meted out to his friend Erickson. So he crouched down and looked through the keyhole. Unluckily he lost his balance, fell forward and knocked his head against the door so hard that it flew open and Halvor came tumbling head first into the class room. He jumped up with a bound, dashed out, slamming the door behind him. He heard the teacher coming after him. He ran into room No. 5 which was empty, shut the door and, putting his back against the door, endeavored to keep it shut. But the teacher was too strong, and Halvor was taken by the collar and asked if he was not ashamed of himself. Halvor turned stubborn and would absolutely not admit that he had done anything wrong by laughing. The other boys had laughed too.

There was nothing more to be done in the matter. But Halvor often had to suffer on account of this affair. Even when he came to class proudly, certain that he knew his lesson perfectly, it might happen that he got stuck. Then he was told that he ought to be ashamed for not knowing anything. He soon learned, however, not to take such things too much to heart. The teachers were not such formidable creatures after all, with one exception—the president. In his classes no one dared but be thoroughly prepared. If they were too busy reading novels or other books and had to neglect something, it was never the subjects which the president taught. With these lessons prepared, they felt comparatively safe.

There were, of course, some boys who conscientiously learned all their lessons. There was, for instance, a big fellow who had lately come from Norway and who interested Halvor very much because he wore Norwegian clothes and took everything so calmly. He worked hard, settling down to his tasks like an old steady horse, while Hermanson and the less ambitious fellows went by fits and starts like young colts.

This serious and good natured boy was nicknamed Full Declaration from the largest division of the Formula of Concord which bore that name, since he was the largest boy at the school, while in contrast, a chunky little fellow was called Epitome. A tall, slim fellow had to endure being called Smalkald Article.

A great lie was circulated about Epitome—a lie which is still alive among the students. It is related that once in Norwegian dictation he walked up to the professor and addressing him with the familiar pronoun, said, "Du Professor, is 'gøtt' spelled with a big G?" The story is obviously made up because a youngster in the lowest class would not have said "Du, Professor" but "Du, Siewers."

There were now signs of spring. The air grew more hazy and balmy every day. The ice became so soft that the skates cut deep into it, causing the boys to fall headlong and slide on their stomachs right into the water and slush along the shore. This watery margin became wider and deeper, so that some girls who had been out in the middle of the ice had to be carried ashore in order not to get wet to their knees. At last the ice began to bulge up in the middle and to groan and crack so that one could see bottom through the rents. And one morning Halvor, who had been out early, came tearing in to his companions with the news that the ice had broken and that great floes were floating down the river which had turned into a rushing torrent and was overflowing all the low lands. That the boys had to go to classes as usual that day was cruel, to say the least. But fortunately it was Saturday, so they had the afternoon off.

The dinners on Saturdays were better than on any other day except Sunday. It usually consisted of fish. But today that did not matter. They could not take time to eat; they had to go and look at the water. Perhaps they might be lucky enough to fall in.

Helgeson, Hermanson, Ueland, Monson and some others of the younger set started up along the river until they came to a place where it ran close up to a steep bank. One great floe after another came floating by. Occasionally one struck against the bank and broke into pieces which continued on their journey over the open sea.

Here was a chance to take a sea voyage. One had only to jump onto one of these floes. They knew very well that it was forbidden pleasure, but what sport it would be. Finally the temptation became too great. Hermanson found a long pole with which he vaulted himself out on a floe which just then swirled close by. He shouted goodbye as he was whirled out into the foaming sea. The others could not resist following him. It would not do to forsake him. They must be ready to fish him out if need be at the risk of their own lives. The floe which just then came along was large enough to hold them all. It bumped into the shore right at their feet. They all jumped on at once and were off to sea. The ice, however, was wretchedly soft. Pieces kept breaking off here and there and at last the tonnage of their raft was insufficient to carry so many passengers. Peder Olson had appointed himself captain and commanded Ueland to jump overboard. But the crew maintained that it was the duty of the captain to sacrifice himself and they were about to shove him off. But before they could do so the floe broke and every man of them slid into the seething flood. Fortunately all of them could swim and it was not far to the shore. They were quite exhausted, however, when they crawled ashore. Still they all agreed it had been great sport—all but Halvor, whose adventures were not yet over. He did not crawl out of the water but onto another floe which was lying nearby and which now started off and carried him to sea again.

In the middle of the sea he grounded on a hillock. There he had to sit in his wet clothes with nothing to do but make the best of if. A comfort in misfortune was that he could see Hermanson a short way off. He had followed Halvor's example and his floe, too, had been grounded. The poor fellow had evidently given up hope of getting his floe afloat again. He was sitting on his pole, resting his chin on his knees. He was close enough so that Halvor could see his nose in bold relief against the evening sky.

"Hey, Rostrum, how are you feeling?"

"Oh, I'm all right. How about you? Are you wet?"

"Of course I'm wet, you boob. Do you suppose a fellow can swim around in this lake for half an hour without getting wet?"

"What do you think Professor Larsen will say about this trip?" asked Hermanson.

"Oh, I guess he will say that we were good boys and that it will be a great blow to our parents to hear that we drowned in such cold water."

"Pshaw! There's no danger. We shall have to wait until someone comes for us. That's all."

"It's easy for you to talk. You're dry. But I'm freezing to death. Come over here and pound me so as to warm me up."

"No thanks. You had better come over here. You can't get wetter than you are."

This did not look so foolish to Halvor, so he waded over to his friend. Just as he stepped onto the edge of the floe it began to move. "Take your pole, Rostrum, and help me shove and you will see that we shall get loose. Then we'll shove ourselves to the shore."

They tried it and were successful. The water had risen so that the floe was about ready to float off and only a slight shove was needed. Upon the cliff behind the college a whole flock of boys stood watching them. Some of them were busy nailing some planks together to make a raft in order to rescue their marooned friends. Professor Larsen appeared on the scene just as the boys had succeeded in getting loose and were steering for the shore. "There stands Professor Larsen," said Halvor. "I only wish he'd come and give me a thrashing to warm me up. I'm freezing so outrageously."

Halvor did get his wish in a way. He did get a pummeling, for as soon as he landed the boys fell upon him assuring him that Professor Larsen had given them orders to see to it that he did not catch cold. They pounded and jostled him about and laughed. And he struck back like a hero until he grew so tired that he had to beg off. It comforted him to know that the other boys had got the same treatment although they had missed his wonderful adventure.

In a few days the ice was gone and the river had gone back to sleep comfortably in its old bed. A few of the hardiest boys began to say that it was time to go swimming. But they were not yet permitted to do so. They might fish, however. Hermanson had a remarkable natural gift in this art. When the other boys, after long and patient trying, were convinced that there was not a single fish in the whole river, Hermanson would stand in the sunshine on shore and haul them in by the score. This was a great puzzle to Halvor. How in the world could the fish know who held the pole? Or, supposing that they did know, why should it give them more pleasure to bite on his hook rather than on anyone else's? But such seemed to be the case at any rate. The two chums were often out fishing together. And when Halvor could not get even a nibble he would ask Hermanson to change places with him. But it did no good. As soon as Hermanson moved, the fish followed him. It was pure witchcraft.

One of the serious drawbacks of the college in Decorah was that the outdoors was so very attractive. It was too hard to study when nature beckoned so enticingly. At least Halvor found it so. While there was skating he, of course, had to practice that sport. And when that was over it was necessary to make daily trips to the river to see if it was warm enough to go swimming. Halvor had never known before that spring was so beautiful. And as a matter of fact, it is not as beautiful in other places as it is in Decorah. Only a few warm days and the whole plateau on which the college stands was dry and one might lie on one's back under a tree sunning oneself and enjoying life in long draughts. The Luther College boys loved spring more than other people. Perhaps it was because they were happier than other people. Life seemed like a beautiful dream to them. There were, to be sure, those pesky lessons which had to be learned, but this labor made their leisure time all the more enjoyable. And perhaps there was some truth to what Professor Larsen was always telling them; namely that the one who does his duty most faithfully is the one who gets most pleasure and benefit out of play.

But if Halvor Helgeson was ever to get through college he would first have to get through the first year. To make a long story short—spring arrived with its Easter holidays; then came summer with Pentecost and the Seventeenth of May. And there was baseball. Before one realized it, it was time to begin to cram for the final examination. The great question was: "Will I pass?"

Hermanson felt safe. He even nourished a secret hope that he might skip a year and get into *Quarta*. Halvor, poor fellow, admitted to himself that if the teachers only knew how very little he knew all hope would be gone. But possibly he might be able to pull the wool over their eyes. If he did not pass it would be out of the question to go home. He could never go home and tell his father that the smartest boy in Springville had flunked. He would have to run away and dig gold somewhere in the Rockies.

The examinations, however, were not so bad after all. Halvor discovered to his surprise that he was one of the smartest in the class and that he was slated for *Quinta* the next year. "For I take it for granted that you are coming back next fall," said Professor Larsen.

Of course he was coming back! Where else in all the world could a fellow have such a good time? What a foolish question!

Home Again

All the boys were ready to leave for home, but money was mighty scarce. They had, of course, all received some money from home which was to have been laid aside for their fare home, but there had been so many expenses during the last days. Some had neglected to send their shirts to the laundry in time and so had to buy new shirts for the closing festivities and the trip. And they had to buy new hats or pay for broken windowpanes so that when the time came there were a number who did not have enough money to buy their tickets. The few who had a little more than enough suddenly found themselves very popular.

"Say, Felland, can you lend me half a dollar? My ticket costs eleven dollars and I've only got ten and a half. Help me out and I'll pay it back in the fall."

Of course, those who had money were generous. But no matter how they figured, there was not enough for all. They were, however, resourceful fellows. A group who were going to Madison figured out that by pooling their money they would have enough to get to Black Earth and would still have a balance of fifteen cents. So they decided to buy their tickets to Black Earth and walk the rest of the way. The fifteen cents, if wisely invested, would supply enough food to keep them from starving on their pilgrimage.

They did not have to go by team to Connover this time because the railroad had been completed to Decorah.

Great was the commotion at the station in Decorah before the tickets were all bought, but it was accomplished without mishap. The boys took complete possession of the train. The conductor was a mere zero. He had lost all authority and merely did what he could to see that no one fell off and was killed. In Connover there was a short wait. At this point they would have to part—some going north and others going east. With their advent the sleepy little town woke up. People rubbed their eyes and sauntered to the station to see what was going on. The boys welcomed them enthusiastically, declaimed Latin to them and offered to bet that Hogstul could lick everyone in Connover. Then came the train and carried off Halvor and the others who were bound for Wisconsin and Illinois.

The number of boys dwindled and dwindled so that when Halvor had changed cars in Milton Junction he was alone. He was not thinking so much about his home now as about his college friends even though all year he had looked forward to the time when he should go home to his father and sister and mother.

Søren stood waiting at the station. For weeks he had been thinking of his boy and rejoicing at the thought of seeing him again. The train came in with a roar, and the first person to appear in the door was Halvor. He was looking very well, was quite tanned, and was wearing a new hat in which his father thought he looked very jaunty.

"Hello, Father!" Halvor could not wait for the train to stop but jumped off and rushed over to his father and began at once to tell him what a good time he had had in Decorah and how much he had learned, and how expert he was at playing baseball and so on, so that Søren could not get in a word edgewise. But he was filled with joy and pride and Halvor could see it plainly.

It was not until they were driving home that Halvor thought to ask about how his mother and Jenny were. His father replied that they were well and would be very happy to see him again.

As they were getting nearer home Halvor found it very interesting to see the houses of their neighbors. It was strange that everything was so unchanged. The old buildings stood there looking exactly as they did before he went away. Well, of course it was not even quite a year that he had been gone, but it seemed much longer than that. Near a couple of the houses were some of the boys whom he knew, so they stopped for a moment to greet them. At last among the many fruit trees he saw the outlines of his own home. It looked very plain after the many big fine buildings he had been seeing. But just the same, how nice it would be to sleep in his old room upstairs again.

Mother and Jenny were standing in the doorway waiting for him. Jenny was shy at first. She had expected him to be a grown-up man by now. But when she saw that he was the same boy as before, she rushed into his arms. Her eyes shone with happiness, and she was so beautiful—much more so than any of the girls he had admired in Decorah.

His mother surprised him by her cordiality. He went to her, shook hands and said, "Thanks for last." The supper table was all set, and Halvor was the guest of honor. The usual supper was of corn meal mush, but tonight they had cream mush, bread and butter, and coffee.

After first having made a trip to the barn to see the horses, cows, and chickens, Halvor sat all evening telling the family about all his experiences. He never grew weary but rambled on about Professor Larsen, and Professor Siewers, and Hermanson, and Ueland, and Monson, and all the other boys. There was no lack of subject matter. How Jenny wished she could see the boys who were so smart and so kind and so jolly—especially the fellow whom Halvor called "Rostrum." Søren was thinking the same, and that he must take a trip to Decorah some time to thank everybody who had been so kind to his boy.

How good it felt to go to bed that night after having traveled so far and after having been up the whole night before. He thought of his friends from school. Surely they must be at home too by this time. Who was the boy from whom he parted last—what was the name of the station—and soon Halvor was sleeping like a log. So soundly did he slumber that when he woke up it was with a start. Where was he? Well, of all things! At home in Springville! Today he must go and see Thrond and Gunhild Knudson.

Gunhild knew that he had come home and was expecting him in the afternoon. She had nagged at poor Thrond until, for the sake of peace, he had put on his Sunday clothes. It was not, she said, as if they were expecting an ordinary farm boy. Thrond should remember that Halvor was studying for the ministry. Thrond limped around busily stuffing the rags out of sight and putting the house in order. He did not know if he even dared to smoke his old pipe now that they were to have such a distinguished guest. When Halvor came, it did not take Thrond long to hear that he had become learned. He had begun to talk like a book. It was only occasionally that he would lapse into the Telemark vernacular. "Isn't it marvelous what book learning will do for a fellow," thought Thrond. "What if our good-for-nothing Knut might have gone to college, too. But that was not to be thought of for such plain folks. It is quite different with Søren who can read and talk English and figger, himself."

Gunhild was not quite so much in awe of Halvor. "You see, I know you so well," she explained. "It was me who received you when you came into the world, and it was me who carried you when you got your name. And I cleaned you up many a time when you were little, and dressed you when you were too small to do it yourself."

How well Halvor knew all this. It was pretty tiresome always to be reminded of it; but, of course, she meant well.

Then he had to regale his admiring audience with telling them about all his wonderful experiences. Thrond said, "Now, I suppose you can read all kinds of books, even those in the very finest print." And when Halvor said he could, Thrond had to move a ways off in order to get a better look at him.

Gunhild had made cream mush, and it floated in its own butter. Halvor had to eat it, and he had to drink coffee—two big cups of it, and it was strong too.

"You must put more sugar in your coffee," said Gunhild.

"No thanks. It's sweet enough."

"Yes, siree! You must take more," and she put three-four spoons of brown sugar in it for him. Halvor had to drink it. It nauseated him, but she meant well and he would not offend her for anything in the world. But it was a relief when the visit was over and he could go home and be sick all by himself.

After a day or two had passed, Halvor had to help with the work on the farm. He had an advantage now, however, in that he needed only to mention that he was tired or had a headache to be allowed to go home and rest. Even his mother realized that he who had studied so hard at the minister school could not stand to work all day from morning till night.

Halvor found it quite embarrassing at times when he met the boys of the neighborhood. Some of them would tip their hats to him just to tease him. And they would call him "The Minister" and imitate his bookish language.

As the summer passed, Halvor began more and more to long to go back to Decorah. Is it not strange about such things? His home was very pleasant. Sister Jenny was blithe and sunny all day long and never tired of hearing college stories. She liked Hermanson and Monson and Ueland and the rest of the boys and felt that she knew them without having seen them. So she was quite a comfort to her brother. He often thought how proud and happy he would be if he could show her off to the boys. They would not be able to help but like her—every last one of them. His father was kinder than ever and his mother hardly ever nagged or scolded, but just the same it was not like being with the college crowd in Decorah. Halvor worked on the farm and counted the days until the first of September when school would open again. In Springville he felt himself to be an outsider. Even between him and his parents there was not quite the same intimacy as before. One day he got into an argument with his father and was more positive than was really necessary or becoming. At last Søren said, "Well, well, my boy—you who have been to college a whole year, of course you know more than me. But when you get a few years older maybe you'll find that you're not so much smarter than me after all."

Halvor felt bad to think he had hurt his father's feelings because, after all, his father did know more than most people. Besides, he was so strong that he could do almost anything—he never lied, and nothing ever frightened him.

There was one thing more that made it hard for Halvor to be at home. His mother now expected him to show concern for the state of her soul and for that of the souls of others in the community. She was surprised to find that was something Halvor could not make himself do.

One day Klemmetsrud met Halvor on the road. He took the occasion to admonish him to use his time well so that he might perhaps succeed in getting his father converted. Halvor flared up and answered him in such a way that Klemmetsrud could only sigh heavily and hasten to inform the brethren that in Decorah boys were taught to be free-thinkers. At least that was what had happened to that boy of Søren's. Well, one needed only talk to him to learn that he had no thought for the importance of saving a soul.

When this was repeated to Anne it caused her grave concern. She did not dare talk to Halvor about the matter. But she often stared at him in a way that made him feel uneasy. She was wondering if the boy's head really was full of dreadful atheism.

Perhaps it was a sin for them to let him learn so much. "For I have always told you, Søren," she explained, "that in my judgment, that as far as I can understand it, no blessing comes of plain folks trying to get so high up and wanting to be better than others. Just talk to Halvor and you will see how queer he acts. I'm sure I don't know whether he believes in God or in the devil or in the Bible. What has become of my darning needle again? I just had it in my hand; is it you who have taken it, Jenny? You had better learn to leave things alone so that I can know where they are. Talk to Halvor, yourself, Søren."

Grown Up

Halvor was happy when the time came to go to town to buy new clothes and get ready to go back to school again. Strange to say, it seemed harder to say goodbye this time than it did the first time. And he had not gotten far on his journey before it came to him that his stay at home had not brought his father much comfort or joy. It was too bad that this was so, for his father had done so much for him and worked like a horse to get him the money he needed. He wished he could turn right around and go home and tell his father how grateful he really was.

Such reflections were soon forgotten, however, for at Milton Junction he met Luther College boys. They greeted each other with boisterous enthusiasm. Oh boy, it was great to see them again!

There is not much to tell about his second trip except that it was as jolly and as noisy as the first one. There was this difference, however. Now he could freely take part in the fun and act the part of guardian angel to the new boys who were going to Decorah for the first time. Could he not direct them in anything and everything? They need have no fear. He would see to it that they reached their destination safely.

Having arrived in Decorah, Halvor sat on his trunk just as he had the year before while being conveyed to the College. This year, however, he was so proud and happy that he began to sing even though he was a monotone. And when he had been to see Professor Larsen and had been registered and had been assigned to his room, and had carried his trunk up to it, and had set up his bed, he hurried down to the other boys and joined them in walking around, sizing up the new boys with as important an air as though he were sole owner of the whole institution.

He was now in *Quinta*. He realized that it was still a great way up to *Prima*. But it seemed nice to be able to look down at the many boys in the class below him. The new boys proved to be very interesting fellows. Some were stylish city boys from Chicago; others were clumsy and awkward farm boys in plain homemade clothes and with big hands that showed that they were used to hard manual labor.

Soon the work of the college was in full swing. Helgeson and Hermanson were again sitting together evenings at the same lamp studying. During the winter of this year Professor Bergh was absent for a time, having been elected to the state legislature. The boys missed him sorely; so much, in fact, that it seemed like a real holiday when he returned and took up his classes again. He was the favorite teacher of the school. He was always friendly and so interesting that the boys looked forward to his classes with pleasure. There was not a student who did not love him.

Halvor Helgeson's second year at college passed very much like the first. He did not distinguish himself. He kept fairly abreast with the others in his class, was friendly to everyone, took part in all games and sports, and let the rest of the world go by as it pleased. The year came to a close and he went home for the summer, to find himself more of an outsider than before.

He had now passed into *Quarta*. He was indeed becoming a man of erudition. For now he would soon be taking up Greek, a fact to which he had often called his parents' attention during the summer. They did not wonder that he was proud. Greek! Just think of it!

It certainly was a task to learn that language. Halvor had lost his courage the minute that Hermanson, who had started to study it during the vacation, told him triumphantly that "to see" in Greek was *horao, opsomai, heoraka, endon.*

Toward the close of this year Halvor was asked to translate a sentence which was supposed to read: "The Lacedaemonians marched into Attica after the Athenians had forsaken their land." Not having the faintest idea of the content of the story, he translated it thus: "The Lacedaemonians used to banish all lazy Athenians to Attica." The teacher bored right through him with his eyes and said, "You should be banished to Attica too, Helgeson."

Halvor was sure that he would not pass the examinations this year. He felt safe in every subject except in Greek. In that subject he knew absolutely nothing, but when the time came his usual good luck came to his aid. He had been growing so fast of late that his pants and coat sleeves were much too short, and he was changing voice. He now spoke in a deep bass voice, but every so often it would crack and produce such a funny sound that the boys would laugh.

When he was to be examined in Greek, he was first given a sentence that was so easy that the whole class knew it. They had often expressed the wish that they might be lucky enough to be asked to translate it in the examination. It consisted merely of the statement, "The Arabs raised many beautiful horses." It was so plain that it was impossible not to get its meaning, and Halvor was the lucky fellow. He translated the stuff about the Arabs and felt that he was not so bad in Greek after all. He was told to continue with the next few lines, which he did not understand at all. He started out, therefore with fear and trembling, but just as he was about to get stuck his voice jumped from bass into a whine which no one could understand, and before he could get his voice under control the teacher said, "Well, that will do." And the torture was over.

When he got home that summer, his mother said, "Why, goodness me, Halvor, how you have grown. You'll soon be as tall as your father."

And it was true. Halvor was almost grown up. New thoughts were surging in his brain, and the world had taken on a new aspect. Strange fires coursed through his veins and he felt a burning desire to sin, let the consequences be what they might. He was given to day dreaming and found life endlessly monotonous. He wanted to get out and gain new experiences.

At home he went about alone much of the time. He could no longer talk freely to his father as he used to do. Still less could he mingle with the other boys of his age in the neighborhood. Why, they didn't know anything. There were many people who thought it strange that Halvor had gotten no further in his studies in three long years. It would not be unreasonable to expect him to be able to preach a sermon. Klemmetsrud was telling that the man who had married his daughter was able to preach without having been to school at all. He even preached in such a way that there was not a dry eye in the audience. And there was Halvor who had been studying for three years and was supposed to be a smart boy, and he couldn't even conduct a prayer meeting. Or perhaps it was the will to do so which he lacked rather than the ability. Klemmetsrud was inclined to think that the latter was the case, and it pleased him mightily to think how disappointed Søren must be in that son of his on whom he had spent so much.

If Søren had any such feeling he at least kept it to himself. He toiled away on the farm, letting Halvor help him when he felt like it, and do as he pleased the rest of the time.

In the fall Halvor returned to school with the same uncomfortable feeling that he had not given his father much pleasure during his stay at home.

He was now beginning the last half of his college course. He found that he was able to carry all that he had learned about with him without much difficulty. It was not so very much. He smiled to think that only three years ago he had thought that the boys up in *Tertia* must possess fabulous erudition.

There were not so very many left of the boys who had begun in his class. Each year there were some who strayed away, so that the class grew smaller and smaller. As a result those who remained felt drawn together all the closer, and there developed among them that intense brotherly affection that one finds only in such a school.

This year there was also a sort of girls' school connected with Luther College. The pupils were half a score of girls who were daughters of professors or ministers. They stayed at the parsonage close to the College and caused the boys much sorrow and vexation.

These girls were so pleasant and attractive that they caused poor Halvor's heart to ache. When this girls' school or *Comitia Dumriana*[7] as it was called, walked along the road he could not keep his eyes off it. He did not care about any one member in particular, but collectively they were irresistible. They caused not only his heart but also his feet to ache. On their account he began to wish to improve his appearance. Conscious of his big feet, he began to force them into shoes so small that they caused him unspeakable agony. He also had to buy clothes oftener than he could afford. What did it matter if he sank into such debt down town that he would not know where to turn when it came to paying it? And what good did all these efforts do him? There was not a single one of the silly fair that would look at him anyway. When he had to chance to talk to one of them it brought him only grief, for he always had to admit to himself afterward that he had made a fool of himself. Nevertheless, he continued using hair oil and torturing his feet.

Under these circumstances it was desperately hard for him to learn his lessons. Even in class time it was next to impossible to listen. His thoughts were engrossed with efforts secretly to work his shoes half off his feet to stop their merciless aching. Then, too, there were wild dreams of all kinds. He was tempted to run away to the new gold mines in the Black Hills. It would be wonderful to sleep out there with a bag of gold dust for a pillow, with a revolver in his hand, and with two more and a bowie knife in the tops of his boots. Out there he would be able to cut loose entirely. And among the riff-raff in the mines and in the gambling dens he would make his name so feared that all business would come to a standstill the moment it was rumored that he had come to town. Fortunately for him, however, the teachers knew nothing of all these terrible plans and regarded Halvor as a perfectly respectable young man.

He was now a man of prominence at the college. He was captain of the baseball team, a leader in the debating society, president of the group of boys who sawed wood for an hour every Friday, inspector of the bedrooms, and he also held a number of minor positions of trust as well. But he often thought with melancholy of how happy he had been the first year when he was among the small potatoes and did not have to struggle with Greek, knew nothing about *Comitia Dumriana*, had no debts, and was not bothered with sinful thoughts and desires. At that time he could safely walk past any store in town. The mention of such firms as Elsworth & Landers, or Olson & Thompson, brought no blush to his cheek. He did not owe them a penny. Those were happy days! Now he could not go to town without thinking how painful it would be to meet one of his creditors. Actually he had not paid for the suit he was wearing. He could not make himself sit down and write to his father and tell him how matters stood. He would not do so except as a last resort. In the meantime he went to classes and took part in all the fun, but his heart was not in it.

Among the students there was a son of the Reverend Mr. Dahlby. He and Halvor became fast friends. What the attraction between them was, neither could say. It was at least not their similarity. Christian Dahlby was a pale, light complexioned young man who often stayed out of games because he was afraid of getting hurt, and he did not go swimming when it was cold for fear of catching cold. As far as such things were concerned it had never occurred to Halvor to worry about his health or to change socks because his feet happened to be wet. What in the world was all this fuss for? But it all made the minister's son more interesting to Halvor. Halvor regarded his friend's solicitude for his body as akin to the delicacy of the princess who could feel a pea through twenty feather beds.

The two boys were soon confiding all their secrets to each other. When Pastor Dahlby came to Decorah a short time before Christmas, he came into Halvor's room in order to meet his son's friend as he expressed it, and to invite him to spend Christmas at his home. The parsonage was a short distance from Decorah. Such an honor Halvor could not decline. He accepted with thanks.

In Pastor Dahlby's congregation there were quite a number of wealthy farmers who sent their sons to Luther College. Each of these boys usually invited one or more of their fellow students to go home with them for Christmas. Many were the loads of college students that were seen driving off to the Halling settlement on the day before Christmas Eve. Conveyances had come for all of them drawn by large well-groomed horses in shiny harnesses with sleighbells. The minister's horses were the best of them all, and his chore boy who drove them assured Halvor when they were going that none of the farmers would be able to keep up with them without breaking the wind of their horses.

Heigh ho, how merrily they trotted along, sometimes in the shelter of woods and then over bare hills where the wind had swept the snow away. When the runners scraped against the stones in these places they shrieked so horribly that the sound went to the very marrow of one's bones. The weather was cold and crisp, and the boys sat stomping their feet on the bottom of the sleigh and pounding each other's backs to keep the blood from congealing. In a little village half way between Decorah and their destination they stopped to rest their horses and to eat and thaw out their noses. It was inexpressibly good to get in to the stove, and it was fun to show off their German to the old German brewer from whom they bought food. He listened to it all without cracking a smile, and he set the boys a bad example by drinking twenty glasses of beer as they looked on.

After an hour's wait they started off again. Now the minister's chore boy intended to make good his boast that he could drive so fast that all the ordinary farm horses would be left far behind. The farmers had no intention of standing for anything of the kind. They were determined to keep up if their horses dropped in their tracks. They had, moreover, this advantage over the minister; they could afford to buy new horses if theirs were wind-broken. And how they raced! The end of it was that the minister's chore boy had to give up his nefarious designs.

Later in the afternoon they began saying goodbye to members of the party at every crossroads. Presently, when they were at the top of a big hill, Christian pointed straight ahead to a big stone church and said that the parsonage lay just a little way off from it among the oak trees. And then it came into view—a long white painted frame building cozily sheltered by great trees.

Halvor felt decidedly ill at ease as he entered the house. But to retreat was impossible. So in he had to go, willy-nilly. It was not long before he felt at home. He had never met such friendly people before. The Reverend Mr. Dahlby was a handsome, rather short man with a closely clipped brown beard and with a skullcap on his head. He welcomed Halvor with a sonorous bass voice and with a hearty handshake. Mrs. Dahlby was so gracious that Halvor immediately felt like calling her mother—and the daughters, of which there were quite a few! Halvor knew one of them after a fashion because she belonged to *Comitia Dumriana,* but he had never dared to talk to her.

The visit to this parsonage was the beginning of a new epoch in Halvor's life. It was his first contact with a happy Christian family life. His home was a fairly good one, but it seemed dark compared with this one. And life in Decorah was jolly and breezy enough, but the boys could hardly be called polite or polished. With them the main thing was to give as good as one got. Halvor was not acquainted with any of the families in Decorah. The only social life he had known there was when he was invited to Brandt's for afternoon coffee on Sundays.

In the house where Halvor was now a guest everyone was happy. At first it seemed almost queer that everyone was so polite to one another. Even in ordinary daily life the pastor was as gallant to his wife and daughters as if company were present. To Halvor this was something quite new, but it appealed to him strongly and left a lasting impression upon him. When the family gathered for prayers mornings and evenings and the father read a chapter of the Bible in his rich bass voice, Halvor knew that he had discovered the wellspring of the love and happiness with which this home abounded.

He had always known that the Bible was a book which one ought to read and from which one might gather wisdom. This had always been impressed upon him at home and in school. But he had not known before that there was something in it that made life more beautiful day by day. That this book was able to bring comfort to those in distress he had heard, but not that it could bring sunshine into the home. That Pastor Dahlby taught him.

On Christmas Eve there was a Christmas tree in the living room. Everyone received gifts and thanked each other and seemed to vie in giving each other pleasure. The tree was to be taken down a few evenings later between Christmas and New Year's, and on this occasion the young people of the congregation were invited to be present.

At church on Christmas Day Halvor met all his college friends who were vacationing in the neighborhood. All of them told him about what a good time they were having and how pleasant it was in the country. In Decorah they were merely boys; here they were students and were looked up to with respect.

Halvor had heard that the Reverend Mr. Dahlby was not a gifted preacher, but he could not understand how anyone could say such a thing. He thought he had never in all his life heard such a good sermon as he heard on this Christmas Day. Even the way the Christmas offering was conducted was uplifting. In great solemnity the oldest and richest men in the congregation went up first and with a formal bow laid their gifts upon the altar. Some of them, who had forgotten to do so before, went directly from the altar to the women's side of the church and gave their wives money so that they too might take part in the offering when their turn came.

The Decorah boys were all invited to the parsonage for dinner, and they all envied Halvor who was privileged to stay there two whole weeks while they had to leave the same evening with the prospect of returning for the Christmas tree party only.

For this party Halvor dressed up as carefully as he possibly could with the few means his little satchel contained. Christian had told him confidentially that he would see the prettiest girl in the state of Iowa. She had a pretty name too—Nora. When the young people were all assembled, Halvor felt a nudge in his side, and Christian whispered: "There she is, over there in the corner, the one with the long braid." Yes, she was good looking, no mistake about that. Little and vivacious, and with heavy brown hair. There was something most remarkable about her eyes. Halvor could not determine what color they were, but they seemed to brighten up the whole room. He could not imagine what had come over him. He could not take his eyes off from her. She had bewitched him completely, even before he had spoken a word to her. A little while later, when she came over with the daughters of the house to meet him, he lost the rest of his sense. She was perfectly at ease. Apparently she did not realize what an honor it was to be conversing with Halvor Helgeson who was said to be the brightest student at the college. Somehow there was such an atmosphere of purity about her that Halvor hardly dared take the hand she offered him when she said good night.

When all the company had left and Christian and Halvor were alone in their bedroom Christian said, "Well, boy, wasn't she mighty good looking?"

"Oh, nothing out of the ordinary." He did, however, make a few nonchalant inquiries as to where she lived, who her parents were, and so forth. She was, he learned, a daughter of one of the best Norwegian families in the neighborhood—very fine people. She was the kind of girl whom all boys worshipped. "And if you can't see that she is beautiful, I don't think much of your taste," said Christian. Halvor apparently did not care whether his taste was admired or not. But in his own mind he thought it was a shame to call Nora Anderson the prettiest girl in the state of Iowa—in the state of Iowa alone. He was sure that her equal had never lived—let us say—in the Nineteenth Century.

One day before the end of the holidays the Dahlby family was invited to Anderson's for dinner. Halvor made a brave show of preferring to stay at home—but of course he could not very well remain at home alone. By daylight he found Nora still more charming. No wonder her father and mother seemed contented with life. Halvor could not understand how Pastor Dahlby could regard her as an ordinary young girl as he actually seemed to do. And her father! He had a right to hold her in his lap but appeared to be too much of a barbarian to care to do so. To make the story brief, when the holidays were over and Halvor, after the two happy weeks, sat driving back to Decorah, he was deep in thought. He had figured out that Easter came on the last of March. Easter vacation began the Wednesday before, which would be the twenty-seventh. It was now the fifth of January. This made it two months and twenty-two days. Then he would be going out to that blessed parsonage that he loved so well. It was a long time to wait. And between him and that time loomed the mid-year examination in Greek, in which he was shaky. Added to that was the necessity of writing a letter of confession to his father and asking him for money to pay his debts.

To the boys at the college he admitted that he had an "awfully" good time during his vacation. But he was careful not to say a word about Nora Anderson. For if he did they would be sure to go right out and get ahead of him.

Halvor braced himself up and forced himself to study. He would have to do so in order to get through, but it was a hard pull. His thoughts seemed to be so unmanageable. He could not keep them where they belonged. Just when they were most needed they would—without his permission—fly out to the Halling settlement to the pleasant parsonage and thence slip over to Anderson's to play around that Nora girl with the shining eyes and the long braids. In general, however, he fared like the rest of the boys—sometimes in favor, and sometimes in disfavor.

The Easter and Pentecost vacations he spent in his friend Christian Dahlby's home. He got only a few fleeting glimpses of Nora Anderson and came back to school more befuddled than ever. Thus passed that year and the next. And before he knew it he found himself actually in the highest class in school. During the summer vacation he had, as usual, been at home with his parents. In his home community he was, of course, a big man, much bigger than at college. His father was proud of his learned son who had grown so tall that his father had to look up to him. To Gunhild and Thrond he was a hero. Thrond had been shown one of his Greek books, and his admiration for one who could read the likes of that knew no bounds. Why, the letters were all upside down, and yet that boy that they had seen grow up, and Gunhild had welcomed into the world, and carried to the baptismal font could read it just as easily as Pastor Harbitz read the Gospel and Epistle.

In Decorah Halvor was, of course, not such a big man. But it gave him a certain sense of pride to reflect that he was now in *Prima*, and therefore was supposed to know a great deal more than the long row of boys below him. Many changes had taken place at the college since he had first come there. The main wing had been remodeled and greatly improved. The south wing had been added, giving the building a much more imposing appearance. And in the tall tower there was now a bell, the funds for the purchase of which had been collected among the students under the leadership of Haatvedt. At the dedication of the bell there was a great celebration, at which Langeland had read a poem he had composed for the occasion. Among other things, this poem declared that the bell would:

> *"Bring out praise and prayer*
> *To the throne of love.*
> *And Haatvedt's name declare*
> *To the stars above."*

Of the teachers of his first year, only the President and Professors Landmark and Siewers were left. Among the new teachers was Professor Jacobsen who had won the love and admiration of all the boys by his friendliness, helpfulness, and prodigious knowledge. He took as much interest in each student as if there were only one. By his work he infused new life into the college. His students could not help catching his enthusiasm for the beautiful, especially for the beauty which is found so abundantly in English literature. Their whole lives were enriched by their contact with him. His love for the good and the pure was an inspiration to them.

Well, of course, boys will be boys even if they happen to be in the highest class in Luther College. And Halvor was no exception.

He cut loose occasionally like the rest and played pranks, so that it is a wonder the patience of the teachers was not exhausted. Occasionally the boys would get it into their heads that it was unreasonable to require them to get up at six o'clock in the morning. One day they tried to remedy matters by tying up the bell so that the man who was to ring it was unable to do so. When he climbed to the belfry to see what was wrong he found the door locked and the key gone. Many such things the teachers had to endure. There was nothing to be done about it. The boys imagined it was fun.

In his last year, too, Halvor spent Christmas at Dahlby's. It was remarkable how keen that man was. One day he frightened Halvor by asking him if he did not want to go with him over to Anderson's.

"No," said Halvor, "I have nothing particular to go there for."

"What's that? You don't suppose you can make me think that there is no one there whom you would like to see? Do you think I am blind?"

And Halvor, who thought his holy shrine was so carefully concealed, got so confused that he could not even assure the pastor that he had seen amiss. Pastor Dahlby was very kind and offered to write to Halvor's father and tell him how matters stood. "Why that is impossible!" exclaimed Halvor, "I don't even know how matters stand myself."

But in a way this conversation brought things to a head in Halvor's own mind and gave him the idea that he ought—no, there was no sense in it—he was not even through Luther College yet. It would be ridiculous. That Pastor Dahlby had seen through his affected indifference was positively uncanny. However, it had its advantages, for he saw to it that Nora was invited to the house to visit his daughters frequently. And so Halvor had every opportunity that he could wish for. They went skiing together down the long hill behind the parsonage. They coasted—half a score boys and girls—on Christian's long bobsled down the road from the post office corner way down into the valley with such terrific speed that it was all the girls could do to hang on, close their eyes tightly and squeal. Halvor always had to take part in this sport as he was the only one who was strong enough to steer such a big load.

"Come up to the study some time this evening, Helgeson, will you?" said Pastor Dahlby one day. In the evening Halvor went up with his heart beating very fast. What could it be that Pastor Dahlby wished to speak to him about? When he was seated , the minister offered him a pipe which Halvor accepted and proceeded at once to light, for he had mastered that art as soon as he became eighteen years old and the rules permitted him to smoke.

Then Pastor Dahlby began: "Well, you do not need to be frightened. There is nothing to be alarmed about. I just wanted to talk to you seriously for once. I believe you are a fine young man and I want to help you if I can. Next year, I take it, you are going to St. Louis to study theology?"

This was something that Halvor had thought very little about. He had been sent to Decorah for the purpose of becoming a minister. He had always taken it as a matter of course that when he was through at Luther he would be going to St. Louis to take up the study of theology, but of late he had had his doubts. He had read a great deal that had made the truth of his religious instruction seem untenable. Now, frankly, he did not know exactly what he did believe. This was something he had never spoken to anyone about. But to Pastor Dahlby, whom he respected so highly, he felt that he could open his heart. He admitted that he had doubts. So many of the things he had been taught he now found hard to believe. He had never passed through a soul-crisis. He had just let things slide and reassured himself by saying that what his teachers had taught him must be true.

"And still you are thinking of becoming a teacher in the church?" said the pastor. "Do you think that is being true to your conscience?" Halvor explained that he did not know. "Well, but you must know. No one has a right to become a minister unless he knows what he believes."

"Of course, it is not certain that I shall finish college this year. There is the examination, you know."

"That, my dear Helgeson, is only subterfuge. I know you will graduate. I have heard that you are a good student, and it will be well for you to think seriously about what you are going into. I have thought about that matter as it concerns you a great deal, and I want to give you a little advice. I cannot, of course, refute all the arguments against the Christian faith which men can think up. There are many difficult questions which I cannot answer. But I have a remedy with which one can sweep away all doubts. It is so simple that anyone can use it. I have learned it from the Word of God which says, 'If any man will do His will, he shall know of the doctrine, whether it be of God, or whether I speak of myself.' If you do not know what you believe you must not undertake to become a minister. The most miserable creature on God's green earth is a minister who is not a minister with his whole heart. But try my remedy. Don't try to dispute away all difficulties, but try to do the will of God according to the law, and you will learn the truth that you are lost and condemned to eternal death. Seek to do His will according to the Gospel, and you will find that you cannot, indeed, of your own reason or strength believe in God; but that the Word not only demands faith. It also creates it. You will perceive that the Word is the eternal life, and to all objections of reason you will be able to say as did he who was blind from birth, 'One thing I know, that, whereas I was blind, now I see.'"

"Well, now, my young friend, I am through with my sermon for this time. But to change the subject—what do you think of Nora Anderson? Don't blush. There is nothing to be ashamed of. And you do not need to answer. I can answer for you both. And if you ever need any help from me I shall give it gladly, for I am fond of both you and Nora."

It may almost be said that this was the turning point in Halvor's life. His mind took on a new seriousness from this hour. He returned to school and he worked hard. It was not only his studies that kept him busy, but many other things as well. He was a leader in the literary society which was planning to put on a program of a more pretentious kind than any which had been given up to this time. And he had to practice his baseball for the big game with the Decorah team which was to take place on the Seventeenth of May. At the program to be given on this occasion he was to represent the student body as a speaker. This made it necessary for him to study up on Norwegian history, a subject which, strange to say, was not in the curriculum of the college at that time. He also was giving much thought to the advice of Pastor Dahlby, but this he kept to himself.

Was it really true—all this about the inspiration of the Bible? Was there really to be a day of judgment? Many good people did not believe in it. The sages of old, many of whom had conceived and expressed ideas so noble that they caused hearts to glow with enthusiasm, had lived and died without knowing the Nazarene. There was no other way. He was always driven back to the same: "If any man will do His will, he shall know of the doctrine whether it be of God, or whether I speak of myself."

He came to no solution, presumably because he did not seek it earnestly enough. But he would give it a trial. He would study theology and would later decide whether or not he had the faith necessary for one who undertook to guide others.

At Easter time when he was out at Dahlby's again he sought opportunities to sit with the pastor in his study talking heart to heart. These discussions were a veritable tonic to him, and the decision to study theology ripened in him day by day.

First, however, he must see to it that he finished his course at Luther College. He must watch his step so that no teacher might have cause for complaint. He did his best to be careful, but ill luck befell him anyway. He and a few other boys had practiced climbing hand over hand along the steel beams under the long bridge across the river instead of walking across the bridge like ordinary people. They thought it was fun to get boys to try it, especially those they felt sure would not be able to make it and would fall kerplunk! into the water. They had induced Atlesen to try it. He got half way across and there he hung begging for help while Halvor stood on the bridge above laughing at him. Atlesen made a couple of attempts to catch hold of the beam with his legs, and then with a bellow of despair he let go and fell into the icy water. The same thing happened to several others. Finally one of them got sick as a result of the icy bath. He explained to Professor Larsen how it had all happened and that it was Helgeson who had invented the sport.

"What are such things for?" asked Professor Larsen. "Can't you understand that one is likely to get sick from falling into the water when it is so cold?"

Halvor could only explain that he had never gotten sick from climbing under the bridge.

"No, not when you don't fall in. But you have induced others to try it and one of them is sick now."

Halvor maintained that it was impossible to know whether a person would fall into the water or not before he had tried the feat. But Professor Larsen would not accept his plea. He told Halvor plainly that hereafter he would expect him to cross the river by means of walking across the bridge as ordinary people did. Halvor regretted very much getting into this scrape just now when it was so important to stand well with the teachers.

It was maddening how many other things he had to attend to just now when he needed all his time to organize what he had learned for the finals.

First came the Seventeenth of May with the address he was to deliver, and with the baseball game. Halvor and the rest of the team were determined to guard the honor of the college, so they practiced every day. It would not do to leave the Philistines down town the least chance of victory. That would be an unendurable disgrace. Halvor simply had to take plenty of time to work at his speech, for the boys had chosen him and they had a right to expect him to do well.

The great day arrived. Halvor was up at dawn. It was a perfect spring day. The air itself was a tonic. In the forenoon the college boys marched with flags and band music through the city streets, with Halvor at the head as standard bearer. He could not help contrasting this occasion with his first Seventeenth of May at college when he and Gerhard Rasmussen brought up the rear as the two smallest boys of the school.

From town up to the college the boys were followed by a great crowd of people in carriages and afoot. The people gathered around a bandstand which had been erected for the occasion in the center of the college park. Many wagonloads of people were arriving from the settlements around Decorah—from Ridgeway and Calmar and Big Canoe and even from Spring Grove. Halvor did not dare look at them. He sat behind a tree thinking about his speech. Up until now he had thought it was really quite good. Strange how it had deteriorated all of a sudden. Now he realized that it was actually stupid. But now he must go forward. The audience was called to order and "Ja, vi elsker" was to be sung. His speech came next. Halvor walked up to the speakers' stand together with the chorus which was to lead the singing. On the way he said to his friend Jensen, "Say, John, you are big and strong. If my speech is too beastly stupid, will you take me down to the river and drown me?"

"You bet. You can depend on me. That is a favor I shall do gladly, my boy."

But when Halvor was on his feet and with quavering voice had begun: "Ladies and gentlemen! On this, the birthday of the new Norway, our thoughts naturally turn to the land that lies in the far north—." At this point Jensen started to clap; the rest followed his example. It was amazing how this helped. Halvor's courage grew apace, and when he ended with "Hurrah for Henrik Wergeland who gave us the Seventeenth of May!" and he noticed that Professor Larsen was clapping too. Halvor then took his seat a proud and happy young man.

We have the speech lying before us and can testify to the fact that it was nothing to brag about, but the student body and the friends of Luther College were an uncritical and appreciative audience.

Now at last Halvor dared look around him. Well, if there weren't Nora and her parents! It was lucky that he had not seen them before. Now he was able to greet them without fear. He could see that the old folks actually felt somewhat flattered by this attention from the main speaker of the day. Halvor took them under his wing and saw to it that they got their dinner and introduced Nora to a select few of his friends—those whom he felt sure would not make too much of an impression upon her. The others he carefully steered away.

The ball game in the afternoon, however, nearly ended in disaster. Those town fellows were shamelessly clever and quick. Time and again Halvor had to get after his men and tell them to be more alert lest the game be lost. Nora was as interested a spectator as anyone, and once as he passed by her she said, "Don 't let those fellows win! I don't see much in the game, but now that you are playing, it won't do to lose. I simply couldn't stand the disgrace."

Halvor was of the same mind, and when he went to bat and the students cheered him with, "Home run, boy, and all three bases full!" he struck so desperately at the ball which came whizzing close to the ground that it flew far out of bounds and way under the speakers' stand which he had graced earlier in the day. And Halvor crossed the home plate while his friends cheered wildly. The victory was won.

In the evening the boys went to the river to bathe their aching limbs, and afterwards they sat around a big campfire on the shore and talked about the great victory. Later, when they got back to the college, they were as hungry as bears. Halvor and the rest had to have something to eat regardless of where they were to get it. Great Eastern was asleep, and all lights were out. One of the boys crept through a window into the pantry and handed out a supply of rusks. The next day the housekeeper made an errand to Professor Larsen and reported that she thought it was the same crowd that had recently emptied a salt cellar into the sweet-soup, thereby rendering it more unpalatable than usual.

Now the year was nearly over, and the boys were talking about how dreadful it would be to flunk. Now they must get down to business and study hard. But how could one study when the weather was so beautiful? It was most unreasonable to have the close of the school year come at this time of the year. It ought either to close just as spring began, or else the college ought to be moved to some place where spring and summer did not tempt one so strongly to loll about sunning oneself on the green. At a meeting in the smoking room, *Niffelheim*, a motion made by Halvor Helgeson to this effect was carried by a great majority. It proposed that a delegation be sent to the Synod meeting for the purpose of advocating that the college be moved to Tierra del Fuego or to some place in the Hudson Bay country. "We do this for the sake of our posterity," said Halvor, "for in such weather no student can, *profecto,* be interested in knowing what '*dagesh forte*' is."[8] This change they could not, of course, expect to have effected in time to benefit themselves.

"The only thing I'm not afraid of," said Halvor to Hermanson, "is World History. Professor Larsen will be sure to ask what the dream of Cyrus' mother was and I know that by heart."

Much as Halvor needed to concentrate on his studies, unavoidable interruptions were always occurring. There was, for

instance, an important lawsuit between Jensen and Bakke to decide
who was to pay for the lamp that had been tipped over and broken
one evening when they were wrestling in the study room. Halvor
had been engaged as counsel for one of the parties, and when his
client won, the judge, the lawyers, and all the witnesses went to town
to enjoy a treat at the expense of the winning party. When they got
home it was so late that they were confronted with the necessity of
getting by the watchman, Crøger, without being discovered.
Accordingly, they waited until they saw the light of his lantern at
one end of the building. Then they stormed up the steps at the
opposite end. But the watchman hurried after them and then made
a trip through the bedrooms where he found everyone sound asleep.
Jensen and Helgeson, however, were snoring so loudly that he grew
suspicious. He lifted the coverlet and found the two fully dressed,
even to their shoes, from which evidence he deduced that they were
among the night owls, and he reported the matter as was his duty.

Two of the boys had been wiser than the rest. They had laid
their coats, vests, and shoes in one of the out buildings and walked
quietly up to their beds under the very nose of Crøger who thought
nothing about the matter except that the butter might have been too
rancid the night before and that they were having katzenjammers.

Then came the last holiday of the year. Halvor fully intended to
use it for studying his Hebrew. But of course this plan came to
naught. Members of the chorus, Idun, decided that they needed a
change of diet and that a way to get it was to take a trip into the
country to sing and forage. They rented a bus with four horses and
started out directly after breakfast. Halvor was invited to go along,
even though he could not sing, because he was so well acquainted
with the farmers and would know where they would receive the most
cordial welcome and the most bountiful fare. The trip took them
out toward Ossian, around to Calmar and Ridgeway, and back to
Decorah. The boys sang well and were so entertaining generally
that they were welcomed everywhere and treated to the best in the

house. They visited and were feasted at Hegg's, Thygesen's, Kittilsby's, and Holstad's and perhaps at even more homes. And they got home too utterly tired to look at their lessons for the next day.

That very day, however, a very heavy weight was lifted off Halvor's mind. Professor Larsen, in reprimanding him for some bagatelle chanced to say in the course of the conversation something about "when you go to St. Louis next fall." Halvor heard no more. It was a sure thing, then, that he would get through the final with a whole skin! Professor Larsen must know and he mentioned his going to St. Louis as casually as if it was a settled matter. The burden of fear that had weighed so heavily upon him had now blown away. Now he could cease dreaming about fearful Greek sentences in which it was impossible to find any sense at all. He was so happy to think he could again sleep with a good conscience until the breakfast bell rang. When one of his friends emptied a syrup can into his trousers just to see how he would act when he jumped into them in the morning, he did not even get angry. He only pulled the trousers off again, took the offender gently but firmly by the neck, held him up against the wall and wiped the syrup off on his hair.

The last weeks of the year were very exciting. Flocks of boys roamed around among the trees singing. It did not matter whether they could sing or not. They were not singing for art's sake, but out of sheer exuberance. The most popular song was one that was sung to the tune of Yankee Doodle. It was really a drill on Greek prepositions and the case governed by each. It began thus:

Preposition *eis* and *hos*
Govern accusative
But, you bet, both *en* and *syr*
Govern only dative.

Anti, epi, mata, para
Peri, pros, and *hypo*
Govern all the cases three
With a little stick-o

And these govern genitive:
Ek, pro---

Well, which ones were they?

And indoors they were playing something called historical authors. The most important events in history were written on small cards. The players quizzed each other on these events by turn. Upon answering correctly a player might put aside a card, and whoever got rid of all his cards first had won the game.

The words Professor Larsen had dropped about Halvor's going to St. Louis gave him courage to write and ask his father if he could not take a week off and come to Decorah for commencement. Søren found the idea a good one, and replied that he would come. It seemed to him that he ought not to begrudge himself this trip after having worked so hard for so many years in order to give his son an education.

A couple of days before commencement he arrived—just in time to take in a thumping good smoker in *Niffelheim* where Halvor acted as master of ceremonies, and, as such, made a ringing speech in tribute to tobacco. Søren was rather surprised at finding college boys engaged in such frivolous pursuits, but he had to admit that Halvor's speech was amusing. He was, in fact, quite elated at merely seeing so many happy boys all together and at observing that his son was one of the best liked of them all.

Such a racket he had never heard in all his life! And the singing! It was all irresistibly amusing.

There was a singing by a chorus which was called the Bremer Musicians. The only entrance requirement of this organization was to be so lacking in musical perception that one was excluded from the regular music classes of the college. Their selection was "Bridal Procession in Hardanger." The high notes at the close—"O ho, O hei"—brought forth such a rare assortment of shrill discords that the audience had to cover their ears.

All of the boys were very attentive to "Helgeson's father." A number of them made speeches in his honor. At last Søren felt that he must make some response and thank them for the honor shown him. He could not, he said, make any speech but he merely wanted to say that meeting Halvor's friends had made him feel twenty years younger, and that if they would accept the price of a couple of boxes of cigars he should thank them once more.

The next evening the graduates were all invited to a supper at Professor Jacobsen's, and of course Halvor's father was included in the invitation. Here the fun was less noisy, but none the less enjoyable. Much of the conversation was above Søren's head, but he rejoiced to think he had a son who understood it all. He and Professor Jacobsen got along famously, and to him Søren confided his pleasure over Halvor's success.

Søren also met Professor Larsen and heard from his own lips that Halvor was a bright young man and that he had behaved very well. This did Søren more good than all the rest, and he felt that now he could go home feeling that he had been well paid for the trip.

The commencement program in the chapel was a very festive occasion, particularly to the young men who were to receive their Bachelor of Arts degrees. It was not a day of unmixed joy. True, they had reached the goal for which they had been striving, but the college had become so very dear to them that the thought of leaving it was painful, indeed. Halvor Helgeson was tempted to wish that he had one year left. It was with joy that he received his diploma from the president's hand and was welcomed into the academic brotherhood, but he felt sad at the thought that now his name would not longer be on the enrollment roster of Luther College and that he must say farewell to a place where he knew and loved even every rocky ledge.

He would have been quite inconsolable if it were not for the fact that the classmates whom he knew the best were also going to St. Louis, so he would not have to part with them in the immediate future. He and these boys had grown up together and had felt drawn closer and closer together as year by year their circle had grown smaller. Those who remained seemed to have become more than brothers. For three years more they would be together. But it would no longer be in Decorah, and this thought made their hearts sore. If Luther College should ever be moved from Decorah, it would no longer be the same school. By the very nature of things the school must remain right where it is—there on the hill, on the very spot where it now stands.

It was with full hearts that Halvor and the other graduates listened to the president's parting address to them. He reminded them that more serious times were now beginning for them. He knew, he said, that they loved Luther College and he felt sure that they would not bring disgrace upon their Alma Mater. He hoped that they would bring joy to him personally. And he wished to stress in particular that no greater joy could come to him than to see his children walk in the way of truth.

The time had come for Halvor to say goodbye to his teachers, roommates, and other friends. And he realized that he would never have such happy days as he had here.

O, golden days, O, life but made
For pleasure and contentment.
When one is young, a student blade,
And harbors no resentment
Toward fate for any other blow
Than that one's mustache grows so slow.

When Halvor was not thinking about the sadness of these farewells, he was earnestly debating with himself as to whether or not he should tell his father about Nora and take him out to visit Pastor Dahlby. But he could not bring himself to it. He had better go back to Springville for the present and possess his soul in patience.

On the journey home the boys seemed as jolly as ever, but Halvor did not feel quite so light hearted, as at each successive station he said goodbye to friends whom he would probably not see again for years. At Milton Junction, Søren treated all the boys who were still together to a dinner. And after that he and Halvor were alone until they reached home.

"What do you think of Luther College and Decorah, Father?"

"Oh, I'm mighty glad I made the trip. I wouldn't have missed it for anything. It was worth a trip around the world just to have a little talk with Professor Jacobsen. And all those boys! For a fellow like me who has been going along alone at home all these years, it was a treat just to look at them. I say, Halvor, I am sure glad that I sent you to Decorah. But let us talk about something else. Next fall I suppose you are going to St. Louis?"

"Well, you are the one to settle that, Father. You're the one who will have to furnish the money, you know."

"Yes, of course, I know that, but is it all settled now that you want to be a minister?"

"Yes, I think so, but I can't be sure of it yet."

All summer Halvor worked hard on the farm. His father reminded him occasionally that it was not necessary to go at it so hard, but Halvor felt that he must have something to keep himself occupied. It was no fun to go around and visit the neighbors. The only ones who he felt it his duty to visit were Thrond and Gunhild Knudson. They had followed his progress at school with as much interest as if he were their very own.

"Because you see," said Gunhild, "it is not as if you was a stranger. You've grown so big and tall and have got so much book learnin' that I s'pose I shouldn't sit and talk to you like this. But you are so kind to come and see us, and now you've just got to stay for supper. And you shall have as good a cup of coffee as I kin make. And I hope you won't take it amiss if I give you these socks which I've knit for you, and may you have health to wear 'em. Thrond has been thinkin' of givin' you a few measly dollars for your trip down to the minister school down in St. Lud—what was it now again that your father called the place?"

And Thrond pulled a bill out of his pocket mumbling something about that it was so little it was a shame to give it, but perhaps Halvor could use it to buy a minister's ruff.

St. Louis

"Well, now, you must be careful not to get lost in Chicago," said Søren Helgeson when his son was starting off to take up the study of theology at the German Concordia Seminary in St. Louis.

To Halvor this advice seemed superfluous. He had not, to be sure, ever been in a metropolis, but he felt that he had traveled quite a bit and was so well able to look out for himself that he would be able to get along anywhere and everywhere. And, besides, it was high time for him to see a little of the world. For this reason he was starting out a few days earlier than was necessary. He wished to have time to look around a bit in Chicago on his way to St. Louis.

As he sat in the railroad coach, he was hoping very much that he would be lucky enough to meet some of his friends in Chicago.

Toward evening he saw evidences that the great city was near. From the window he saw great factories and long rows of frame houses scattered here and there over the prairie, and then again the open plains on which grew mostly white painted billboards announcing that at precisely that spot lots could be purchased at the lowest possible prices and on the best terms.

At last the train was brave enough to plunge right into the thick cloud of smoke that hid the city from view. And a short time later it stopped in the midst of the noise and the stench. Halvor followed the other passengers out and suddenly found himself standing on the street amid a deafening roar dickering with a great number of men, all of whom wished to drive him to his hotel. He managed to

[155]

fend them all off, and thought he was quite a fellow to be able to do so. But very soon afterwards his pride received a sad blow as he discovered that he was only a green boy from the country after all. He, a graduate from a Latin school who thought he knew everything, could actually be made a fool by a ragged little bootblack! This bootblack had evidently sized him up at once. He walked up to Halvor and offered to shine his boots. Naturally Halvor thought it would not be a bad idea to have his boots shined before he left the city. When the work was done he offered the boy ten cents. The little scamp refused the money with the greatest scorn. He was not, he said, an ordinary bootblack, of the kind that was found everywhere on the streets. His price was twenty-five cents. He seemed so authoritative that Halvor paid him what he demanded, only to have a bystander tell him that five cents was the usual price. How it galled him! He did not so much mind losing those few pennies, but it mortified him to know that he showed so plainly that he was from the country.

Now that he had begun to spruce up, he might as well get his unruly locks cut, he thought. He soon found an unpretentious place in a basement. When the negro who appeared to be boss of the place stroked his face and told him that he needed a shave as well as a haircut, Halvor did not even have the courage to tell him that his face was still as smooth as a newly laid egg, which was the truth of the matter. He was only too glad to escape from the place alive. He soon found his way to a plain looking hotel and engaged a room for the night.

This done he went out and spent some time wandering around, growing dizzy from looking at the multitudinous shops stretching for miles and miles in every direction. There were brilliantly lighted saloons glittering with gilt and mirrors, interspersed with rotten wooden houses in front of which sat ragged and dirty women with half starved children in their arms. There were other shabby houses where drunken women, both black and white, were standing in the doorways, pouring forth curses and obscenities. Some of them were hanging out of the windows, their painted faces leering horribly at the men who were passing by.

On a street corner stood a man in a wagon baking waffles and crying his wares, and beside him sat an old blind woman turning a hand organ with one hand and holding out a tin box for alms with the other. It was all of it most nauseating. Recalling his experience with the bootblack, Halvor had backbone enough to say no when a black-bearded man with a black eye and smelling strongly of whiskey sidled up to him and in a hoarse voice told him that he had been sick in the hospital for two months and begged for a little money for food and lodging.

Halvor managed to find his way back to the hotel but in doing so he was almost run over by a fire engine which with wildly galloping horses came tearing down the street followed by a great crowd of men and women hurrying and scurrying that they might feast their eyes on the horrors of a fire.

Now that he was safe at the hotel Halvor thought he had earned the right to indulge in a cigar. It calmed him and helped him think. What in the world did all these people live by? From where did all the supernumerary shopkeepers get their trade? And those awful women with their sodden painted faces! For shame! How much nastiness there was in the world! Halvor felt as if he had besmirched his soul by even looking at them.

Stepping out of the hotel for a breath of air, Halvor was accosted by a very amiable individual who said that he had taken to him at sight because of his honest face. He offered to take him to a very cozy place where they could play cards in peace. When Halvor declined the invitation, the man became still more affable and assured Halvor that by his refusal he had risen still higher in favor. Cards, he said, were best avoided, and finding Halvor to be such an exemplary young man he had decided to do him a good turn. He had, he said, by chance come into possession of a gold watch which he would sell very cheap since he already had a watch and needed a little cash. Selling it for twenty dollars would be giving it away, he said. But since he had taken such a fancy to Halvor he would let him have it for fifteen. It hurt Halvor very much to have to decline the offer, but he could not buy a new watch. The old silver one which his father had given him would have to do.

When it was time to get ready to leave for St. Louis new trials awaited him. When he inquired about the station from which his train would leave for St. Louis, no one in Chicago would admit that there was such a place as St. Louis. Some insisted that they at least had never heard of a town by that name; others admitted that there was a cemetery by that name somewhere way down in the southwest. Chicago and St. Louis were at that time of about equal size and were therefore bitter rivals. By the same token Halvor found when he got to St. Louis that people there would pretend that they had only the faintest recollection of having heard a floating rumor to the effect that somewhere or other there was a village named Chicago. At last, however, Halvor found a man in Chicago who was willing to admit that there really was a dump of a town named St. Louis and that the train for said town left from the station nearby on Canal Street.

The journey to St. Louis took him through a great number of beautiful small towns surrounded by cornfields billowing over the plain. The two hundred and fifty miles were covered in nine hours, and at dusk the train rumbled over a great bridge and through a tunnel a mile long and finally stopped in a great basement room from which travelers ascended broad stairs to the surface of the earth and found themselves in the center of the city.

It was not until Halvor noted the great size of the city which was so little known in Chicago that he remembered that he had not the slightest idea of where to find Concordia Seminary. This was a detail which he had completely forgotten. Since it was evening, he decided to go to a hotel for the night and then start out early the next morning to look for the school. He did not think to look in a directory but started out on a hit or miss hunt.

In the course of the day he visited a number of schools, none of which was the right one. Just as he was beginning to get discouraged, he ran across a German saloonkeeper in the southwest end of the city who said he did not know any school named Concordia, but that yonder big gray brick building down on the corner was Saxony College, and that in the house behind it lived Professors Guenther and Schaller, and in the one a little farther north lived Professor Walther. Another man who chanced to come along explained that the school was sometimes called Concordia Seminary.

With a great sigh of relief Halvor started walking toward the building. Just then he heard a voice say, "Well, well, there comes Helgeson too!" And looking up he saw Hermanson, Gabrielson, and a number of other old friends.

"Great guns! How good it is to see you after tramping around all day and asking the way in German."

"But why in the world didn't you find that out before you started out?"

"You said it! Why didn't I? Haven't you discovered before now what a blooming idiot I am?"

The Seminary building was quite spacious to look at from the outside. But it was planned so poorly that a number of the rooms could not be used because the access to them was so inconvenient. It had been erected at three different periods by as many architects, each of whom had paid no attention to the work of his predecessors. All three had obviously been drunk when they drew their plans. From the main wing one could not get to either of the side wings without going through all the bedrooms, up a few stairs, out onto a veranda and then into whichever side wing one wished to reach.

It was an unwritten law at the seminary that three of the best rooms should be set aside for the Norwegian students of which there were about twenty in Halvor's day, as compared to five times as many Germans. Before the "Practical Seminary" had been moved to Springfield the enrollment at the school had been much larger. At that time the Norwegian students were quartered in various other buildings in the neighborhood. The room which housed the greatest number of them was called "Hututu."

Halvor found that his best friends had reserved a room for him in Asgaard which was the best of the rooms assigned to the Norwegians. It was located close to the stairs at the left in the second story of the main wing. The room next to Asgaard but at a slightly higher elevation was Valhalla. It might just as well have been at the other end of town, however, so difficult of access it was. In the basement of the main wing was the dining room where a buxom housekeeper, Frau Jungkunz, went about seeing to it that no one ate too much. Directly above this dining room was the auditorium or *Aula* as it was called where the students met to protest when the board became too frugal.

After getting comfortably settled in Asgaard, Halvor went over to announce his arrival to Professor Walther. He was shown up to the study where the Professor sat in the midst of a great pile of papers and books, with a long German pipe in his mouth. He was a very thin old man with a little fringe of hair around his neck and ears which was seemingly tied together by a band of gray beard under his chin. His eyes were deep-set and clear and his large aquiline nose almost touched his chin.

He rose at once: "Well, my dear young friend, I suppose you are one of the new students."

Halvor began to explain who he was and so forth, but he found to his chagrin that he could not speak German as glibly as he had thought. He managed to give his name, however, and to present his credentials from Luther College.

"Then you are one of our dear Norwegian students? You are heartily welcome! Our Norwegian brethren have always brought us joy. You will receive information from any one of the older students as to what books you will need to buy and so forth." And with a cordial handshake and a *"God keep you, my young friend,"* he dismissed Halvor and returned to his work.

As soon as the classes began, the Norwegian students realized that it would be hard for them to keep up with the Germans. They had to get used to speaking German, and that was not an easy thing to do. For four or five hours each day they had to listen to lectures and take notes for dear life. And in the evening when they tried to go over their notes in preparation for the quiz the next day they usually found them as hard to decipher as if they had been in Assyrian cuneiform writing.

The Germans had the advantage of knowing the language better, and many of them were able to use shorthand. As a whole they were able young men. They were a little younger than their Norwegian classmates as a rule. They came from the *Gymnasium* at Fort Wayne in their wild state, but they gradually learned the ways of the world as they pursued their theological studies. And when they had finished their seminary course they were prepared to take the most poorly paid positions and work like slaves and suffer if need be for the sake of purity of doctrine.

All of the teachers at the seminary were old fashioned and very scholarly. Professor Schaller was always so friendly that one could not help but love him. Professor Guenther was dry and taciturn, but was said to possess unfathomable learning. The students said of him that he resembled General von Moltke in being able to be silent in a score of different languages. Then there was old Pastor Brohm who was able to walk back and forth in the *Aula* with his hands behind his back and teach Hebrew although he was blind with old age because he knew the Bible by heart in Hebrew.

And first and last there was Professor Walther himself. By reason of his strong personality he seemed to Halvor and all the other students to be the very incarnation of simple child-like faith and profound scholarship. His lectures were given in a hall in the library which was near his home. He always appeared for his classes on the stroke of the clock, and he demanded the same promptness from his students. As a teacher he was strict; bluffing he would not tolerate. The favorite class of all the week, and the one by which the students counted time, was the so-called Luther Hour when Professor Walther lectured in the *Aula* on a subject selected by the students themselves and during which they sat puffing at their pipes and taking down in their notebooks some expression or other which they found extraordinarily striking.

One might have thought that the few Norwegian students would have felt like strangers among so many Germans, but such was by no means the case. There was the most cordial comradeship between them. The teachers made no difference between them and the Germans unless it was to show the Norwegian students, whom they regarded in a way as guests, a little more attention and confidence than the others. The reputation of the Norwegian students at St. Louis was excellent. It was taken for granted that all of them were exemplary young men. They were welcomed into the best families among the German congregations and almost always got the best *Waschtante*.

This last expression needs an explanation. Every non-resident student was assigned to a family with the understanding that he might consider himself a member of it while he was a student at the Seminary. In this home his clothes were washed and mended. And for this reason the mother of the house was called his *Waschtante* or wash-aunt. There were always enough kindly disposed families ready to take in students and do for them in this way.

Halvor was assigned to the home of a well-to-do elderly widow who from the very first day seemed to regard him as a near and dear relative. This hospitable arrangement was much appreciated by the boys because the board at the Seminary was certainly nothing to brag about. The students as a rule could not afford to pay for lordly fare; and, besides, the German school authorities seemed to think a young man would take hold of his theological studies with greater zeal if he were constantly hungry.

Halvor could not stand it. He thought with longing of the fleshpots at home. He and the other inmates of Asgaard bought a frying pan, and when the fare had been too German for a few days, they would nickel-up and buy sausage and other good things and have a feast in all frugality.

Living so economically made the Christmas and Easter holidays, which were spent in the homes of hospitable Germans near Collinsville, Illinois, seem all the more festive. They went there in a body and were always made to feel welcome. In the beginning, it was told, these Germans had never seen any Norwegians and were surprised to find that they were ordinary white people and not a kind of Eskimo.

The Germans at Collinsville were very capable and enterprising people. There were not many of them, but they had their own church, schoolhouse, parsonage, and teacherage. They had their own minister and two regularly hired teachers. Like all genuine German Lutherans they were very *gemüthlich,* and they seemed to be on a surprisingly familiar footing with the Lord. They always spoke of *Der liebe Gott* as a respected member of the family, one whose will one must be only too glad to do in all contingencies.

Professor Walther was the minister of a large congregation in St. Louis. It was, however, divided into four districts, each of which had its own church with an assistant pastor. It was, therefore, only occasionally that Professor Walther himself preached in each of these churches. When it was known that he was to preach at a certain one of these churches, the Norwegian students used to make it a point to attend there. By following him from church to church, it often happened that they heard the same sermon more than once because he always wrote his sermons and committed them to memory. Occasionally Professor Walther took the place of the organist in the church nearest the Seminary. The students who had not been present were then very much put out over not having known that he was to play.

The Norwegian students also went occasionally to one of the German churches to hear the old giant, Pastor Buenger, thunder against the Papacy and its teachings. But as a rule they attended the services of a little Danish congregation which met in one of the schoolhouses of a German congregation. Here they took turns preaching as the congregation had no pastor.

Here, toward the close of the year, Halvor Helgeson was to preach his first sermon. He had worked on it for three months, and yet when the time came he felt that it came far short of what a sermon should be. He needed more time, and he did not know whether he dared preach in the first place. He was so uncertain. But after a great deal of encouragement from other older students he took courage and said he would try. He had, moreover, just read George Eliot's *Romola* and had been thinking a great deal about Savonarola, the great forerunner of the Reformation. Even this courageous hero of the Christian faith said that he "often had to preach on the faith he had yesterday in hopes that it would come back to him tomorrow."

Halvor, then, preached his sermon with fear and trembling. He had learned it well and delivered it fluently. But when it was over, he slipped quietly over to his *Waschtante*. It was hard to look his companions in the face—for they knew all the foolish pranks he had played in Decorah. But when he met them again they comforted him by saying that his sermon was really pretty good. One of them said it had been almost too much according to formula and a little too obvious. It reminded him, he said, of the famous disposition:

"We will today consider together the subject of 'The Two Disciples on the Way to Emmaus. 'We shall see: First, how many there were. And second, whither they were going."

Halvor had now struggled through the first year and was enjoying the prospect of the summer vacation when he might go north and be with Norwegian people once more. The Germans were all right, but they were aliens all the same. His father had sent him the money and given him permission to go home by way of Decorah in order that he might attend the Synod Meeting which was to be held in Decorah that year.

The school year at the Seminary was not over until the last of June, but the teachers had been impressed with the fact that the Norwegian students, coming as they did from a land so far north, could not stand the hot summer weather of St. Louis, and gave them special permission to leave earlier than the Germans. Halvor and the other Norwegian students who were not among the graduates of that year, left early in June, traveling by steamboat up the Mississippi to McGregor. This was slow travel, to be sure, but that was all the better. They were in no hurry.

What an enjoyable trip they had, with nothing to worry about! Whenever the boat stopped long enough, they took a walk up into the city to see the sights. And they amused themselves by watching the roustabouts working and sweating. And they saw to it that they got to the table first when the dinner bell rang. At night, too, it was pleasant to lie on the deck, smoking and viewing the many tall dark spooks between which the boat plowed its way.

Among the passengers was a Roman Catholic priest. A couple of the students thought it their duty as orthodox Lutheran students to put to use what they had learned at St. Louis and try to convince him of the heterodoxy of the Papacy. For a whole day they strove to convert him, but to no avail. He remained obdurate and could not even be made to admit what to Halvor Helgeson was especially important, namely, that the clergy should be allowed to marry.

Every once in a while the boat grounded on a sand bar, and there was a long struggle to get it afloat again. But Halvor did not mind in the least. He had paid for transportation with board and lodging to McGregor even if it should take a month to get there. In spite of everything, however, it took only five days for the boat to land at McGregor. The same afternoon Halvor stepped off the train at Decorah.

Great guns, but it seemed good to see Decorah and Luther College again after a whole year's absence! And to revisit all the old haunts and to sit at the table with the boys in the dining hall! Well, if they didn't have the very same maids! And to go swimming again in the very same place where years ago he had learned to swim. Everything was a treat. Halvor felt that he was still just a boy. In the evening he betook himself to the smoking room in the "Chicken Coop," where he heard a lively debate. It seemed that a bed bug had just been found in a tobacco box. Jensen had proposed that it be admitted as an advisory member of the society. Someone else made a substitute motion that it should merely be invited to take a seat. This matter it was that caused the heated debate.

Because of the Synod meeting, classes at Luther College were discontinued a few days before the regular time. Halvor was very happy to be able to be present at the commencement exercises as well as at a party given in honor of Professor Tandmark who was going back to Norway to live.

This Synod meeting, which was the last one held before the church body was divided into three districts, drew a great crowd of people to Decorah. Halvor Helgeson and the other students from St. Louis were invited to act as advisory members as was the custom. At this a couple of boys grinned at Halvor from across the hall to remind him of the debate the night before.

In addition to the many splendid men who came as delegates there were a few queer ducks who helped make the meeting interesting to anyone who, like Halvor, had a sense of humor. One man, for instance, who was about to take part in a doctrinal discussion prefaced his remarks thus: "I am only a layman and have no book learning, but I have uncommonly good judgment and understanding."

Thinking it might pay him to get acquainted with such a man, Halvor sought him out after the meeting and engaged him in conversation. The man was now more at his ease and talked quite freely: "Norway is," he said, "what I call as good as a heathen country. They learn nothing but the catechism and the question book. I'm a bright fellow, you see; but I never got no book learning."

"But in this country things are better in that respect," ventured Halvor.

"Oh, yes, but I was too old to learn anything here. And, you know, we have such a funny minister where I live. The only thing he thinks about is to rake in the money. He's mighty good at that. Every winter at New Year's he gets up a party and invites all who are behind with their church dues. And after giving us a good meal he duns us. Naturally we can't refuse for the looks of it. Then he puts the money out at high interest."

"This isn't the first Synod meeting you've attended, is it?"

"No, I've been to one before. At that meeting I managed to push through a motion that they had been fussing over for years. I says: 'Preus, says I, I give all the Norwegian ministers in America, says I, power and authority to start good Norwegian parochial schools, says I.' And Ottesen—you know Ottesen at Kaskeland—he says, 'I second the motion.' And the motion was carried."

After the Synod meeting Halvor drove home with Pastor Dahlby and visited at the parsonage for a couple of weeks. And since he was so near, it was only reasonable that he called at Anderson's once in a while. It was especially in the late afternoon that he did so. Nora was teaching school in the neighborhood and was not at home during the day—not that it mattered at all. Mr. Anderson was a very intelligent fellow, and it was for the sake of talking to him that Halvor made his calls. As the distance was so short it was not much trouble to go via the schoolhouse. And it was, of course, mere coincidence that he would usually be walking by the schoolhouse at the time when Nora was leaving for home. Naturally he would walk with her. They talked a great deal about indifferent matters. And Halvor found that she grew more charming every day.

The only fly in the ointment was her little sister who went to her school and who would insist on walking home with them. It was most exasperating! It was impossible to get a real talk with Nora with that kid tagging along. But one afternoon Nora had sent her home first. And quite by chance Halvor happened to come along that very day, and just at the right time. Nora—the little witch—looked as if she suspected him of having something on his mind. And it proved to be even so. When they had reached the valley they sat down on the trunk of a tree to rest for a moment, and Halvor said:

"Nora, I want to tell you something. If it were not for the fact that students at the Seminary are forbidden to become engaged, I would ask you a question. But now I shall have to put it off for two whole years. I want you to know, however, that I shall ask it then. What do you think you will answer then?"

And Nora looked down and whispered, "I think I shall answer yes."

"I hope you will not change your mind. Be sure not to let anyone come and take you away from me in the meantime." And that was all. It was just so prosaic.

When Halvor got back to the parsonage, Pastor Dahlby said, "Well, I see you have been at Anderson's again. You look so happy. May I congratulate?"

"No," stammered Halvor. "It is against the rules at St. Louis for a student to have any other sweetheart than theology."

"Well, but something has happened," said the minister. "What is it?"

"Oh, nothing, except that I asked Nora what she would say in two years when I ask her to marry me.

"And what did she reply?"

"She thought she would answer yes."

"Well, that is a great way to obey the rules of the Seminary! Do not be afraid, however. In such matters one does not follow rules."

Now Halvor went home to spend the rest of the summer with his parent before returning to St. Louis.

"It certainly took you an awfully long time to get here from Decorah," said Halvor's father when he arrived at last.

"I've been on a visit at Pastor Dahlby's," said Halvor. "And there is something else I think I should tell you. Near the parsonage there is a family named Anderson. There is a girl there who I like. Her name is Nora."

"But, my dear boy, wouldn't it be best to wait with such things until you are dry behind the ears? Let me see, how old are you?"

"Why, don't you know? I'm just old enough to vote for Tilden for president this fall."

Søren gave such a start that he forgot Nora and everything else, such a pain did it give him to think that Halvor would vote for the Democrat, Tilden. "What are you saying, boy? So that's what you learn in St. Louis. If I thought you were serious I would—"

"No, no, I'm not serious, Father. I shall, of course, vote for Hayes. I meant only that I am twenty-one."

"Well, so you are. How you frightened me with your Tilden talk!"

And Søren felt so relieved to know that Halvor had not become a Democrat, after all, that he had nothing more to say about Nora.

Since Halvor was now a theological student, he was, of course, invited to preach in his home church. Everyone had been waiting for years to hear "that there boy of Søren Helgeson's."

So he preached his one and only sermon one Sunday morning. When he had mounted the pulpit he caught sight of his father and mother sitting in the front row with misty eyes and his knees began to shake. Beside them sat Thrond and Gunhild Knudson, happy in the certainty that now at least they would hear a preacher who was the equal of even Pastor Harbitz.

Halvor did himself proud and everyone marveled at his fluency and at how well he knew his Bible. They did not know that he had worked at that sermon for three months and could have preached it in his sleep.

The next day when Halvor visited his godparents he was received with greater respect than ever before. "But it don't seem like we should call him Halvor any more," said Gunhild to Thrond. "Say, what is it we should call you, Halvor? We seen your name in print in *Maanedstidende,* and it said 'Stud Helgeson.' What kind of titulation is that to give a fellow, I should like to know?"

Halvor explained that it meant only student.

"Well, wasn't that what I told you, Thrond, that it was nothing to get mad about. But I guess we'll have to call you Halvor, anyway, seeing we've always known you. You know it was me that brought you into the world."

"Yes, of course. Call me Halvor. That name is good enough for me."

"It seems queer to think how learned you've got to be," said Thrond. "But then you've got a learned father, too. If I was as learned as him and could read and write and reckon like he can, I wouldn't go slaving around here on a farm."

"What would you do?"

"Oh, I'd go down to Chicago and get a job in the stock-yards."

Halvor spent this summer working on the farm. He worked so hard that his father thought it was too much of a good thing and that he was over-doing.

In due time he went back to St. Louis where the second year passed much as the first had done, except that this year the studies grew more and more interesting. In fact, the year ended all too soon. He was at home again during the summer vacation and he preached a couple of sermons that he had written in St. Louis. In the middle of August he said to his father one day, "Well, now you'll be glad to know that this is the last year you'll have to give me money. And if you think you can afford it, I'd like to leave now and go by way of Decorah so as to visit Pastor Dahlby."

"Oh, yes, I guess that will be all right. You may do as you like. But you might just as well tell the truth and say that it is not Pastor Dahlby but someone else that you are so set on seeing."

After having seen for himself that all was well in the Halling settlement, Halvor reached St. Louis in time for the opening of school.

There was so much to be learned the last year that he did not see how he could accomplish it all. But he did his best. Professor Walther's lectures to the third year students every Thursday evening on what he called *Die Getrunkene Wissenschaft* were so replete with wisdom that Halvor wished he could have heard them one year more. The same was true of his lectures on pastoral theology. They gave the students a new outlook upon the work that lay before them and made grown men out of what had up to that time been boys. For once Halvor had no fear of the final examination. He had learned his Baier's *Dogmatics* by heart and could rattle off the paragraph on "Of what does the pure doctrine consist?" At the examination it was shown that he was able to translate a chapter of the Old Testament from Hebrew to Latin, that he knew the mode of procedure in church discipline, that he could give an account of the introduction of the Reformation to the Scandinavian countries, that he could give the contents of the explanation of the eighth commandment in the Greater Catechism, and that he knew what the heretics, Socinus and Cochlaeus believed concerning the Millennium.

He was therefore given a diploma stating that he had studied theology with great diligence, that he had lived an exemplary life,

[171]

and that the examination had demonstrated that he was well prepared. The above was attested in behalf of the faculty by C. F.W. Walther, S.S. Theologiae doctor et professor.

Halvor had already, through the Church Council, received a letter of call from several small congregations in Morris County, Minnesota, and had decided to accept it. No one could suspect him of taking the call for the sake of money for in the letter of call the congregation stated expressly that it "could promise no fixed salary but that the members would contribute to the frugal support of the minister according to their means."

After saying goodbye to his teachers, *Waschtante* and other friends in St. Louis, Halvor paid another visit to Decorah. Here he was at once reminded that he was no longer a schoolboy but a theological candidate when Professor Larsen used the pronoun "De" in addressing him. He proceeded out to the parsonage and to Anderson's. He could wait no longer. He told Nora's parents his errand with no beating around the bush. They replied that Nora must suit herself. Then he got hold of Nora.

"It is your intention, of course, to move to Morris County as soon as I have been there and got a home built for us."

"How do you know what my intentions are?"

"You haven't forgotten what you promised, have you?"

"No, but I might have changed my mind since then."

"Have you changed it?"

"No, I haven't."

"Oh, my darling, Nora! How happy you have made me!" The rest will have to be left to the imagination. The printed page cannot do justice to it.

A month later Gunhild Knudson read the following in *Kirketidende* as she sat in her home in Springville:

"On the sixth Sunday after Trinity, the twenty-eighth of July, in Red Wing, Candidate Halvor Helgeson was ordained to the holy ministry by the President of Minnesota District, the Reverend B. J.

Muus. The ordination sermon was preached by the Reverend Mr. Bøkman. The following vita was read: 'Halvor Helgeson'—now listen, Thrond,--'was born on the fifteenth day of July, 1855, in Springville, Wisconsin'—yes, I remember it as if it were yesterday—'of the parents Søren Helgeson and wife, born Holte'—Why that isn't true, Thrond, Signe was born in Tuddal. I've heard her tell it myself. 'In his home he received a good bringing up and was confirmed at the age of fourteen by Pastor Evensen. Immediately after confirmation, in the fall of 1869 he entered Luther College in Decorah, Iowa, at which institution he completed the prescribed courses. Thereupon he attended the Theoretical Theological Seminary in St. Louis where he studied for three years. At the examination held this summer he was found to be well prepared for the holy office of the ministry. He has now accepted a call from Trinity and Six Mile congregations in Morris County, Minnesota.'"

And as Gunhild wiped her eyes she added, "Ain't it strange to be sittin' here reading about him? And Anne says he is engaged, and that she is rich too. And me that has known him since he was born!"

"Yes, fellows like him they generally gets the one they want. There was Pastor Harbitz. He was married to the daughter of a captain, named—well, if I ain't forgot the name!"

Pastor Helgeson

Young Pastor Helgeson had already worked for half a year in his congregation. His parishioners had received him with cordiality, but they had very little else to offer him. It was hard work. He had to travel far and wide to organize congregations among the settlers. Now he had so many that he was barely able to reach them all once a month. It was perhaps best that he had no home of his own. He had to write to his father and ask him for money to buy a horse and buggy. He got the money, but was cheated in the deal so that he now had to rattle over the great prairie with an old nag that was barely able to hang together. Lodging he had to seek in the cabins of the settlers wherever he chanced to be. These consisted usually of only one room, and when the minister came he would sleep with the man of the house in the bed while the wife and children slept in the box-bed on the floor.

Halvor made the best of things and was as cheerful as ever. He was welcome everywhere. They thought he was rather young and jolly to be a preacher, but none the less they found his visit refreshing. The congregations at this time were pestered by sundry fly-by-night preachers who went from house to house frightening people by their lurid talk of hell fire and God's wrath. Halvor had to go the rounds after them, airing out the houses after their visits, and by word and example impress upon his people that God is good, and that one of the Christian's first duties is to be happy.

There was also another species of the tramp order, too, who traveled about making capital of the credulity of the settlers. One day as Pastor Helgeson passed the schoolhouse in which he was to preach, he noticed a placard nailed to the door. It read thus:

"A lekjer or address will be held here next Sunday afternoon at four o'clock by Halvor Pederson. For his subject he will take, 'Is it true that there is a life after this?' The lekjer will be a presentation of both sides of the question in the light of nature alone without reference to the Bible. All who would like to hear a philosophical subject scientifically handled is cordially welcome. Admission 10 cents."

With such learned lecturers Halvor had many a battle.

People thought it was marvelous how well he managed to get around in all sorts of weather. When the winter storms had made roads so impassable that hardly anyone dared leave the house, he would shovel his way through the snowdrifts.

He had hoped that his Christmas offering would be big enough so that he might get himself a little house and go and get Nora. But at Christmas time the weather was such that he was almost alone in breaking the way to the schoolhouses where he was to preach. This was a great disappointment.

It was not until several months later that he was able to write and tell Nora that he now had a parsonage. The house was, he wrote, only sixteen feet short and twelve feet narrow, and there were only two small rooms. But if she would come it would be changed into a veritable palace. And Pastor Helgeson scraped together a little money and went down to the Halling settlement and came back richer than he had even been before.

The people of his congregations could not help but like Nora. It was impossible not to do so. As she found it tiresome to stay at home alone so much, she nearly always went with him on his drives. When they had the opportunity of staying at home for a few days it was a festival for them both. The house was so clean and neat and the mistress of it so charming and sweet that Halvor would forget that he was a dignified clergyman and would put his arms around her, lift her off the floor and dance around her. "My darling Nora, I'm as happy as twenty kings."

A year passed and another and there was peace in the congregations until the controversy over predestination broke out.

We shall pay a short visit to the young pastor and his wife.

One would hardly recognize the house. An addition had been built so that there were now four rooms. In one of them there was actually a carpet. And over by the stove there was a cradle. Nora and a maid were busy in the kitchen. Very frequently Nora went to the window and looked down the road because Halvor had gone to town to meet his father who was going to visit them for the first time. Søren had not been able to be at the wedding and had not seen his daughter-in-law as yet.

There they came! And Nora ran out to meet them. She could see at a glance that the tall man with the blond beard was Halvor's father. Halvor would look just like him when he grew older, she thought. Going straight to Søren she gave him a kiss, and he held her at arms length and looked at her and said to himself that love had certainly not been blind in Halvor's case.

But there was another man in the buggy, a little old lame fellow who climbed down. "Well, Nora, who do you think this is? It's our old neighbor, Thrond Knudson, whom I often have told you about. Wasn't it nice that he came too?"

After they had entered the house and had looked at little Søren who lay in the cradle, and after they had eaten, Nora sat telling Thrond how glad she was to see him. Søren felt so honored by her graciousness to his friend that he had to give vent to his feelings in some way, so he took a bill out of his pocketbook and laid it in little Søren's cradle.

"Now, Father, you must tell us all about everything in Springville."

"Oh, there isn't so much to tell. Mother is well, and Jenny is engaged to our new minister. There is trouble in the congregation again. People are disputing about Calvinism and synergism or whatever 'ism' if may be. And it looks as if there will be another split."

"On which side are you, Thrond?"

"Well, I s'pose I'll have to be on the same side as Gunhild; she knows all about such things. And she says she wants to be on the same side as Preus. I guess they call it Missouri or Mississippi or something like it."

"Are you having the same trouble here, Halvor?" asked Søren.

"No, it is still quite peaceful here. They talk more about the price of wheat than about predestination and election. There is just one woman who bothers me a little. She comes and complains about her husband. She weeps and says, 'You see, Lasse, he is a Missourian, you see; and so he says that if he only does not commit suicide, then it is the Lord who is sponsebel for what happens to him.' But that is about the only one who gives us any trouble."

"What is your opinion, Halvor, about this question of election?"

"Oh, to tell the truth I'm not lying awake nights thinking about it. But I believe in all simplicity what a certain man has said, namely, that one cannot expect to be elected if one refuses to be a candidate."

"Well, that's about what I think, too. That's a big fine boy you have there, Halvor. What's he going to be when he grows up?"

"It's too early to decide that. But if we live that long, I shall follow my father's example and send him to Luther College in Decorah."

ENDNOTES

1) Page 6: _Indiland_: The "Indian Country," a term used by the Norwegian settlers to describe lands in east-central Wisconsin, especially in Waupaca and Portage counties, but also sometimes included Winnebago and Waushara counties. The Neenah settlement, later known as Winchester (Springville in this novel) is located in Winnebago County.

2) Page 9: _Squared:_ A corruption of "squired," that is, married by a "squire" (a judge or justice of the peace).

3) Page 10: _Stas:_ A Norwegian term that means "finery" or "Sunday best." It is here confused with _stats,_ meaning "state," implying the official state church of Norway. Because of the vestments of the clergy, replete with a white ruff, the two terms sometimes were confused.

4) Page 46: _Pastor Evenson:_ A fictional disguise for the Rev. Even J. Homme, the first resident pastor of the Winchester congregation. Homme was very active in recruiting boys from his parish to attend Luther College. Later, he founded the town of Wittenberg in Shawano County, Wisconsin, and its institutions of charity (orphan's home, old people's home, etc.).

5) Page 47: _Kaskeland:_ A corruption of "Koshkonong," the large and prosperous settlement of Norwegians in Dane and Jefferson counties, Wisconsin.

6) Page 90: _Primaner:_ The Latin name for a member of the highest or "senior" class at Luther College. The following Latin terms were used to describe the classes: _prima_ = "senior," _secunda_ = "junior," _tertia_ = "sophomore,"

quarta = "freshman," *quinta* = "second year preparatory," *sexta* = "first year preparatory." The preparatory department at Luther College was dropped in 1928.

7) Page 131: <u>*Comita Dumriana:*</u> A schoolboy Latin term for the female students meaning "assembly of the silly fair."

8) Page 147: <u>*Dagesh forte:*</u> A term used in Hebrew grammar. The boys in the upper classes at Luther College studied Hebrew in preparation for their theological studies.

Wisconsin's Native Son

By

Prof. Gerald Thorson

One autumn day in 1869 a thirteen-year-old boy entered the office of Lauritz Larsen, president of Luther College in Decorah, Iowa. From behind the desk Professor Larsen looked up to greet the young boy: "And what is your name?"

"I am Peder Olsen, from Winchester, Wisconsin."

"Oh! You are from Pastor Homme's congregation. Is Olsen the only name you have? That's too common a name."

The young boy replied that he had no other name. At that point one of the other faculty members, the Rev. Nils Brandt, who was also in the room, spoke up. He had been the young boy's pastor in Winchester before he joined the faculty at Luther College, and he informed the president that the young boy's family name in Norway was Strømme.

"Well, then," Professor Larsen said, "that's what we'll call you." And that year the young boy's name appeared in the college catalog as Peder Strømme. [1]

So it was that Wisconsin's native son received his name—a name that in the years following was to be known far beyond the regions of his birthplace. Just when Peder was changed to Peer is not clear, but he was named after his step-grandfather, Peer Snekker, the second husband of his grandmother, who had immigrated to

Wisconsin with two children by her previous marriage. At any rate, the young fellow became Peer Strømme, instead of Peder Olsen, son of Ole Olsen, escaping the fate of innumerable Norwegians—a fate described by another Wisconsin author, Ole Buslett of Waupaca, who wrote in one of his novels, *The Saga-Chair:*

"His right name was Ole Olson Ausa [in English, a dipper or ladle], but like so many others of us he has changed his name to Ole Dipper. Then he dropped his English Dipper and is now only Ole Olson. But now we have so many Ole Olsons in each community—we have Big Ole, Little Ole, Thick Ole, Small Ole, and all the sons of Ole—that all of Norwegian-America goes by the name of Ole Olson." [2]

Peer Strømme's name, on the other hand, is indicative not only of his free spirit; it also suggests the way in which his life's work was achieved by his immersion into the immigrant culture in which he was raised. This immigrant culture the American historian, Theodore Blegen has called a half-way house:

"So the immigrant lived in a Norwegian-American domain, not quite forsaking the people he came from, not quite a stranger to the people he came to. He was on the bridge of transition. He was making his way into American life. In short, he was a Norwegian-American." [3]

Peer Strømme was not an immigrant, but he was brought up and spent much of his life in an immigrant culture. He was a Norwegian-American.

A product of a culture which was in the process of creating its own identity in a new environment, Peer Strømme went on to become a popular and well-known figure among the Norwegian immigrants. Educated in, and informed about, both Norwegian traditions and American customs, he drew his values not only from these two cultures but also from a third, which was neither American nor Norwegian, but in the process of change and discovery. That this hyphenated cultural group would later be so modified as to be indistinguishable from the American culture does not alter the fact that Peer Strømme himself was deeply influenced by an ever-changing cultural pattern. At the same time, his career led him beyond the boundaries of a parochial immigrant group to participate in the larger scenes available to a talented young man in late nineteenth century America. These opportunities were there, however, because he availed himself of both worlds. A native-born American, nurtured in a pioneer immigrant society, a society still speaking a foreign language, Peer Strømme found himself and his vision in his immigrant heritage. And it is this that delineated his contributions and strengthened his achievements.

Strømme's initial cultural experiences came in the Winchester settlement in east-central Wisconsin. Born there in 1856, the third of thirteen children of Ole and Eli Olsen, Strømme grew up in an infant settlement of Norwegians. His father, who had come to America at age fifteen with his step-father, mother, and sister in 1844, had later joined his parents in their move from the Muskego settlement southwest of Milwaukee to the Winchester forests in Winnebago County in 1850, three years after the first Norwegians had arrived in the area. Two years later, in 1852, Ole married Eli Haugen, and their wedding was the first to be recorded in the church record book in Winchester.

Strømme has described the settlement in his memoirs, published after his death, and used many events from his early experiences there in his first novel, *Halvor*. His home, a log cabin on the wooded land, was the scene of many gatherings and frequent visitors, some of them coming to see his father in his role as justice of the peace. The chief influences in the shaping of his vision and life were the church and its pastors, the school, the Norwegian newspapers, and the advent of the Civil War. The settlement was practically devoid of musical and artistic activities and there was no library, but the boy read all he could lay his hands on.

The young Peer early caught the attention of teachers and preachers. One year he won all six prizes in the local school. His parents decided then that he should become either a lawyer or a minister. Through the influence of the first resident pastor in Winchester, the Rev. E. J. Homme, he was sent, in 1869, at the age of thirteen, to Luther College in Decorah, Iowa, even though the requirements at the time were that students should be fourteen and confirmed. Strømme was neither. He has related how the day before he left he was given his first cup of coffee. His suitcase was packed, and on top lay two pairs of trousers which his grandmother had made for him from material she had carded, spun, dyed, and woven: "and so she had sewn the trousers extra large in order that I could have room to grow in them. They had blue and gray stripes up and down and were meant to be beautiful; but I suffered much sorrow because of the trousers after I joined the other boys in Decorah. They made fun of them and said, 'Where'ja git them pants?'" [4]

Strømme's years at Luther College extended and deepened his cultural experiences. These were essentially Norwegian-Amer-ican in nature, but his education, grounded in the classics and languages (Greek, Latin, Hebrew, Norwegian, German, and English), opened up many new vistas. It is here that his love of literature was fostered; here he became acquainted with the writings of Henrik Ibsen, William Shakespeare, Geoffrey Chaucer, Charles Dickens, and Mark Twain—to mention only a few of his favorites.

Strømme graduated from Luther College in 1876. That same year he went on to study theology at the German school, Concordia Seminary in St. Louis, Missouri, to prepare for the Lutheran ministry. Spending three years there, with summers occupied mainly in preaching at various Norwegian churches, Strømme graduated from Concordia Seminary and was ordained into the ministry of the Lutheran Church in 1879 at a meeting of the Norwegian Synod in Northfield, Minnesota.

Called to assist the Rev. Bjug Harstad in preaching and establishing congregations among the Norwegian settlers in the Red River Valley, Strømme left that summer for Hendrum, Minnesota. That fall he went to Lansing, Iowa, to marry Laura Marie Erickson and returned with her to the primitive conditions of the frontier settlement. During the seven years that he was there, he established several congregations, serving as many as seven of them at one time, and achieved a reputation as a man with fast horses.

It is important to note that, in the Red River Valley, Peer Strømme was once again thrust into a pioneer settlement, a Norwegian community in the process of building and transforming the American frontier. The first Norwegians had arrived in the area only seven years before. This time, however, he was one of the active participants in the process of building a community. He became active in local politics, and in 1881 he was elected superintendent of schools for Norman County, a post he held for five years.

In 1886 Strømme left the Red River Valley for Nelson, Wisconsin, to serve other Norwegian congregations. Restless and uncertain in the ministry, finding his interests and his talents demanding another career, Strømme did not hesitate when the opportunity came to leave the ministry. And so in the fall of 1887 he went to St. Olaf College in Northfield to become an instructor in mathematics, English, Norwegian, German, and history. In January, 1888, however, after only one semester, he resigned his position to move to Chicago to edit the Norwegian language newspaper *Norden*. From then until his death in 1921 Strømme was associated with journalism, either as an editor or a correspondent. During those years he wrote for several different newspapers in Chicago, Superior, Madison, Minneapolis, and Grand Forks. He spent one year as editor of *Vor Tid* (Minneapolis, 1904-5), a political magazine; and in 1909-10 he edited the literary magazine *Eidsvold* in Grand Forks. He became one of the best-known writers in the

Norwegian-American press, but he also wrote for such English language newspapers as the Minneapolis *Times,* the Minneapolis *Star,* the Chicago *Times,* and the *Wisconsin State Journal.*

During these years he also wrote fiction and poetry and became recognized, as Ole Rølvaag once noted, [5] as the best translator that Norwegian America produced. His translations from Norwegian to English, English to Norwegian, German to Norwegian, and Swedish to English included a wide variety of materials—fiction, non-fiction, and poetry.

It is as lecturer, translator, author, journalist, that Strømme achieved a mark of distinction among Norwegian Americans. His was a career both limited and made significant by the major influences of his life: the pioneer settlements of the Norwegians in Wisconsin and the Red River Valley, the urban Norwegian colony in Chicago, and his education at Luther College and Concordia Seminary, with its classical and theological emphases. These did most to shape his views and inspire his artistic vision. In all these places he lived in a culture in the process of transition, and this culture provided the creative impulse for this gifted man.

As a speaker Strømme was in great demand. He was known as a witty humorist who could entertain and inform on a wide variety of subjects. His greatest contribution here was probably made in his political campaign speeches. A Democrat among Republicans, Strømme enjoyed telling of the time he met Dar Reese, the Republican State Chairman for Minnesota, in St. Paul, and introduced him to his son. "Well," Reese said, " I suppose that you have brought up your son to be a good Democrat."

"Two things I have taught him," Strømme replied: "to fear God and to vote the Democratic ticket."

Reese replied: "Well, any man who votes the Democratic ticket has damned good reasons to fear God!" [6]

Strømme was frequently called on by the Democratic party to campaign in the Norwegian communities. He participated in the campaigns for Cleveland in 1888 and 1892 and for Bryan in 1896, speaking primarily in Wisconsin. But his influence went beyond the Norwegian communities. In 1908 the national Democratic party requested him to tour the southern states on behalf of John A. Johnson, Minnesota's governor, as a nominee for president. He was once president of the Chicago Scandinavian Democratic Club, and he served as vice-president of the Chicago Democratic Club. He himself never held political office, but at one time he fully expected that his efforts on the campaign trail for others would result in his appointment as governor of Alaska. [7]

As a translator Strømme provided the Norwegian immigrants with translations of several books, most of them published by the John Anderson Publishing Company of Chicago. Among these were Gustav Frenssen's *Jørn Uhl,* Murat Halstead's *The Illustrated Life of William McKinley, Our Martyred President,* James W. Gerard's *My Four Years in Germany,* at least five of Byron A. Dunn's Civil War novels, Stanley Waterloo's *The Story of Ab,* and other works of popular American fiction. At the same time he insured that some of the Norwegian classics would be known to the English-speaking community. He translated several poems from Norwegian and Swedish in English, including Aasmund Vinje's "Fedreminne" and two hymn texts which are still sung in American congregations: Magnus Bostrup Landstad's *Der mange skal komme fra øst og fra vest* and Thomas Kingo's *Skriv deg, Jesu, paa mit hjerte.* Strømme himself thought that his translation into English of Bishop Laache's *Book of Family Prayer* would remain as his finest contribution. [8]

Strømme's major achievements as a journalist are to be found in his political essays and his travel letters. In 1890 he made his first trip to Norway, and in the first two decades of the twentieth century he was in Europe at least five different times. He made two trips around the world, one in 1911-13, the second in 1913-14; and reports of these attracted wide attention in the Norwegian-American communities, with their typical Strømme penchant for detail and humor. Some of these were later collected and published as a separate volume. [9]

Shortly before Strømme's death the editor of the *Wisconsin State Journal* requested him to write a series of reminiscences as a journalist. He completed seven of these before his death in September, 1921, and these were published posthumously in November and December of that year as "My Red Letter Days As a Newspaper Man." None of the articles dealt with his work as editor of Norwegian-American newspapers; all were concerned with his travels.

Strømme's first article focused on his visits to Norway, beginning with his first trip there in 1890, which he described as the return of an exile, even though he had never been there before. He was in Norway in 1906 for the coronation of King Haakon and participated in the centennial celebration of Norway's independence, May 17, 1914. He told how he met the king of Norway and of his visit with Norway's author, Arne Garborg. In his second article Strømme described his visit with Selma Lagerlof, the Swedish author whom he regarded as one of the major novelists of the time. The third article focused on London, the city of his dreams. He went there in 1906, primarily in pursuit of scenes made popular in the novels of Dickens. In 1911 he was there for the coronation of King George. During one of these visits he was made an honorary member of the London Press Club. His visits to Germany, described in his fourth article, reveal his fascination for Berlin and German culture. He was there in 1911 and then again in 1915 as a war correspondent. The final three articles dealt with his travels in Poland and Russia, his trip to Europe in 1912 with agricultural experts from the United States, and his visit to China in 1911, where he found Shanghai to be "the liveliest and most cosmopolitan of all large cities."

As an author Peer Strømme became best known for two of his novels, though he wrote three. He also wrote several short stories, innumerable critical essays and book reviews, and he also published a book of poetry and one of memoirs. His first novel, *Halvor,* began as a serial in the Superior *Posten* in the fall of 1892 to boost the circulation of the newspaper he had just purchased. It was later published in book form and has had two previous translations into English. [10]

Halvor, the story of the son of Søren and Signe Helgeson of Springville, Wisconsin, is drawn from his own childhood experiences in the Winchester community. He describes the clearing of the land, the building of homes, and the organization of the church in the pre-Civil War days. Historically accurate facts and authentic persons appear along with the fictional characters. Here, for example, are the pioneer pastors Preus, Duus, and Brandt, the traveling lay preacher Eielsen, the Luther College president Larsen, and the pioneer editors Fleisher, Langeland, and Johnson. Here is sketched the pioneer social and religious life—the building of the church, confirmation, the country school, the wedding celebrations, charivaris, funerals, and the saloon. Here, too, is described the impact of the Civil War on the lives of the immigrants: Halvor's father joins the men as they go off to fight the war.

Always these scenes are presented with humor, irony, sometimes sarcasm—Strømme's literary trademarks. When he writes of the saloon, for example, he tells about Ole Findreng, a Civil War veteran, who gets drunk and hangs himself. Ole's friend, Myran, the saloonkeeper, who saw to it that Ole received his whiskey, later reflects on how lucky he is "that this happened just now when Ole did not owe him more than a dollar or two. He would be magnanimous and let the widow off from paying this debt."

The congregation gets a church and a resident pastor, but before long contention arises because some of the members feel that the Synod pastor is too worldly. They search about to find something which will bring his dismissal: "But to depose him for preaching against drunkenness, or miserliness would not look good. . . It must be on account of false doctrine or a wicked life. Preferably on account of false doctrine; that seemed the most proper reason. But it was hard to catch Pastor Evenson in that . . ."

"Luckily, however, the great controversy about slavery arose at this time. Pastor Clausen had just resigned from the Norwegian Synod because that body would not declare that under all circumstances it was a sin to be a slave or to keep slaves. Among the congregations everywhere there was great excitement. The ministers were compelled to take a stand. There was talk of hanging Professor Larsen because in an explanation demanded by *Emigranten* he had said that he had heard good reasons for the right of a state to secede from the Union. Klemmetsrud and his friends were much interested and pleased, for this was something to hold to. They read *Emigranten* and *Skandinaven* and were sure that everything Fleisher, Langeland, Johnson and others wrote was the gospel truth. And there it was in black and white that a clergy-man of the Norwegian Synod approved of and defended slavery, an institution which many of the members of the congregation had risked their lives to abolish."

Since Pastor Evensen is a member of the Synod, the congregation is sure that he too is a defender of slavery. A church meeting is called.

"It was testified under oath that the Reverend Mr. Evensen had told an old man that he was too old to be saved. It was proved that he had refused to allow one of the first members of the congregation to partake of the sacrament of the altar, and that in general he had been stubborn and self-willed, so that it was patent that he had forgotten that he was not his own master but a servant whom the congregation had hired for four hundred dollars a year plus festival offerings and fees for ministerial services, the amount of which was to be determined by the means and inclination of the giver. Thus ended the investigation. The new congregation erected a church edifice beside the old one, in which place it stands today as a monument to the late sainted Klemmetsrud."

Halvor is considered to be ministerial timber, and one very hot Sunday in church "Halvor sat squeezed in between his father and another man and suffered intensely. It was so roasting hot and so muggy, and he needed so desperately to scratch his back, but could not get to do so, squeezed as he was. The minister seemed never to get through the sermon. At last the boy's sufferings became so great that his patience gave out completely. He began to cry, and then at last he was allowed to go out." But to the older parishioners it became quite clear that the young son of Søren Helgeson had been greatly affected by the sermon; such a young man should be educated for the ministry. The next year Halvor goes off to Luther College, where Strømme relates many an amusing incident of school life, and follows this later with studies at Concordia Seminary. In a final chapter the immigrant's son is a minister in the Red River Valley.

Strømme's second novel continues the adventures of Halvor, this time as a pastor among the Norwegians in the Red River Valley. *Young Helgeson,* first published as a serial in *Normanden* in 1906, appeared in book form in 1911. [11] Strømme's humor and irony are still present in this novel, but there is even more satire in it. Here, as in the first novel, we have an historically accurate background: the great blizzard of 1879-80, the organization of a town (the Norwegians dream of calling it St. Olaf, like the "big towns" of St. Paul and St. Louis, but it is finally christened Noraville), a Fourth of July celebration, frontier journalism, the saloon, the introduction of politics, the establishment of local government, and the church struggle over predestination, which was at its height among Norwegian Lutherans in the 1880's. In all this the young Pastor Helgeson plays his part.

While *Halvor* was almost entirely Norwegian-American in its focus, *Young Helgeson* shows more of the encroaching American influence in the life of the Norwegian pioneer. Here there are several American characters, and we get more of the Norwegian settler's entrance into American life, especially his growing participation in politics. Probably the most interesting section of the book is chapter five, which details humorously the congressional battle for the "bloody fifth" district between two Republican candidates, C. E. Kindred and Knute Nelson. For satirical comment Strømme singles out a newspaper editor, politicians, and a student pastor from Augsburg Seminary in Minneapolis. In the final chapter of the novel, Pastor Helgeson goes to Norway, where people are constantly amazed that he can speak Norwegian. He explains that in America there is also a Norway, with good Norwegian schools and Norwegian teachers from Norway. There are even many people born in America, he says, who use no speech but their parents' Norwegian dialect. But "that this could be true, people in Norway seemed to have difficulty in believing."

Strømme intended to write a sequel to these two novels where the chief character was to be the son of Pastor Helgeson, but the story never appeared. Instead, for the subject of his third novel, he went to the Norwegian colony in Chicago. His many years as a newspaper editor had acquainted him with both the Norwegians and Americans there. That he had previously considered the Norwegians in Chicago as material for a novel can be seen in a comment he wrote in the Superior *Posten* in 1892. Before long, he said, he would begin another story (*Halvor* was then running serially) with the title "From the Fashionable World." He added, "It is an attempt to create a picture of life among our prominent countrymen from Chicago, and we believe that it will be interesting." It is not likely that he had then planned the story which he finally wrote, but he was at least aware of the possibilities that existed for a novel based on the life of the Norwegians in Chicago.

In the Clutches of the Devil,[12] the story of Nils Holmsen and Halfdan Moe, Oslo University students who have immigrated to Chicago, is a novel of decadence imitative of Hans Jaeger's *Fra Kristiania-Bohemen* and growing out of Strømme's reading of the literary naturalists. Aware that the novel would elicit unfavorable reactions, he purported to be translating a manuscript left by one of the protagonists of the novel.

The novel opens with a Chicago newspaper account of the suicide of Nils Holmsen. Reading the account is Halfdan Moe, who, the reporter in the newspaper states, is one "whom drink and other horrors have completely ruined." The preceding evening the two men had discussed suicide. Nils took his life, but Halfdan, who was dying of tuberculosis, instead sold the revolver, went to a sanatorium, and there was in the process of writing his memoirs. We are then taken back to Oslo, where the family backgrounds and the progressive degeneration of the two young university students is related. Since the two agree that they cannot become ministers ("I wasn't handsome enough—nor dumb enough"), they settle on becoming literary men. They get infrequent jobs translating "some bloodcurdling American dime novels" into Norwegian before deciding to move to Chicago, for many years the cultural center of Norwegian America. They fare no better in the new world than they did in Norway. They eke out a bare subsistence by translating, join a group of Norwegian freethinkers, among them Marcus Thrane, and dissipate among the journalists of Chicago.

Strømme's fiction is a spirited account of life among the Norwegians in the United States. In each of his novels his chief concern is to tell a story, and this he does well, creating in each a different dominant mood. Strømme was one of the first Norwegian Americans to display a definite talent in his fiction; his work reflects the influence of both European and American literary traditions. It is an interesting and valuable testament to the author's imaginative grasp of the life of the immigrant, taking its place among the best that Norwegian America has produced.

Peer Strømme was no ordinary citizen. As a gifted, creative, and productive writer, he has bequeathed to subsequent generations source materials for their understanding of the Norwegian-American community, for it is that community that provided the subject matter for most of his work, as well as the inspiration and the creative impulse. Like all good artists, though, he both recorded and interpreted in order to provide penetrating insights into the immigrant mind. More important than the records he left us of that community, however, was the contribution he made to the culture and the experience of that community in its period of transition, in its struggles to achieve an identity in the new world. He enlarged the immigrants' perspectives, opening up new vistas. At the same time he allowed them, perhaps demanded them, to retain their heritage and their language while not being bound by them in the quest for happiness and welfare. Strømme knew, and his writings reveal, as Willa Cather understood, that Americanism is Europeanism meeting the challenge of a new environment in its own terms.

Peer Strømme, then, Wisconsin's native son, was a product of two worlds at their meeting point. In finding the best of two worlds, by pursuing the path of the union of the two, neglecting neither one for the other, he was able to find his own identity in the American scene and to devote his life to those creative impulses which would allow the immigrant to fulfill the promise expected of him in his search for the new earth.

NOTES

1) Peer Strømme, *Erindringer* (Minneapolis, 1923), p. 46

2) Ole Buslett, *Sagastolen* (Chicago, 1908), p. 118

3) Theodore C. Blegen, *Norwegian Migration to America: The American Transition* (Northfield, 1940), p. 81

4) *Erindringer*, p. 42.

5) Theodore Jorgenson and Nora O. Solum, *Ole Edvart Rølvaag: A Biography* (New York, 1939), p. 301.

6) Letter, R. J. Strømme to Gerald Thorson, March 10, 1948.

7) *Erindringer*, p. 317.

8) *Erindringer*, p. 383.

9) *Breve fra Peer Strømme paa reise rundt verden som "Normandens" korrespondent* (Grand Forks, 1911).

10) *Hvorledes Halvor blev prest* (Decorah, 1893; Grand Forks, 1910); *How Halvor Became a Minister,* translated by Inga Bredeson Norstog (Minneapolis, 1936); *Halvor: A Story of Pioneer Youth,* translated by Inga B. Norstog and David T. Nelson (Decorah, 1960).

11) *Unge Helgeson* (Grand Forks, 1911).

12) *Den vonde ivold* (Grand Forks, 1910).